Velvet Seekers:
Africans Orbiting These Parts

Kwabena O. Akurang-Parry

Langaa Research & Publishing CIG
Mankon, Bamenda

Publisher
Langaa RPCIG
Langaa Research & Publishing Common Initiative Group
P.O. Box 902 Mankon
Bamenda
North West Region
Cameroon
Langaagrp@gmail.com
www.langaa-rpcig.net

Distributed in and outside N. America by African Books
Collective
orders@africanbookscollective.com
www.africanbookscollective.com

ISBN-10: 9956-553-56-5

ISBN-13: 978-9956-553-56-3

Dedication

I dedicate this to the evergreen memory of
Yaa Amene Akurang-Parry (June 4, 1998-November
15, 2015). My beloved daughter, Yaa, Rest in Peace

Velvet Seekers:
Songs of Africans Orbiting These Parts

Part Two: The False Dream

Trapped in the chilling vortex of perennial winter
Of These Parts
Oh of These Parts
Mother Africa
We shall no longer cross the Sahara to harvest tomatoes
We shall no longer cross the southern Trump wall
Ah! Mother
Your children everywhere
The sufferers
Oh! In These Parts
Symbolized by skyscrapers
Allegories of civilizations
Ah! The gilded These Parts
Of sanguinary pits
Of racist holes
Of Trumpian holes
Of bottomless ones
Of subterranean ones
Of cavernous ones
Ah! All trumpeted and sanitized
Ah! The gilded holes of These Parts
The civilized gilded holes of These Parts
Cultured gilded holes of These Parts
With the elegant cockroaches of Washington
With the choreographing bubonic rats of New York
Oh these gilded craters of civilization
These gilded holes of These Parts
Brilliantly sanitized
But elegantly depressive
Droppings of cacophonic democracy
Trumpeting the "Other!"
Sanitizing gilded holes of These Parts
Deeper holes of These Parts

Gilded holes for mass killers
Gilded holes for individualism
Gilded holes for alienation
Gilded holes for dehumanization
Gilded holes for homelessness
Gilded holes for drug users

Part Two: The Return

Ah Mother Africa
Your children everywhere
The lone sufferers in These Parts
Gilded holes of These Parts
Holes of winter
Holes of racism
Holes of marginalization

Mother
Your soothing warm winds

Mother
Are luring us to return home

Mother
We are home-bound to blossom again

Mother
The Trumpists devoured our tap roots

Mother
Trumpist termites in their gilded holes

Mother
They devoured our tap roots

Mother
We are coming home to rejuvenate in your sun

Mother
The Trumpists' guillotine decapitated us

Mother
Yet, we are coming home to wear your royal crown

Mother
Our lungs are full of pollutants of These Parts
Pollutants from gilded holes of These Parts
Ah! Big droppings of cacophonic pollutants
Pollutants of cacophonic democracy
We are orphans orbiting their super-power gilded holes

Mother
We are coming home to take in your purity

Mother
We are coming home for your ancient pathways of
freedoms

Mother
We have been buried in the variegated autumn of their
gilded holes

Mother
Yet, your graceful Harmattan will lull us back to life

Mother
Your siblings gave us visas to orbit in their gilded holes

Mother
They are building walls along their gilded holes

Mother
We are coming home to receive your eternal birthright

Mother
Let them thump their chests and trumpet their din
Mother let them trump their whole-fullness
Let These Parts sanitize their gilded holes

Ah! Let These Parts deodorize their gilded holes

Mother
Your Saharan winds of purity from the ancient hills

Mother
Will caress us to rest in your pure arms again

Mother
We shall leave their gilded holes of Otherizing
We shall leave their gilded holes of hegemony
We shall leave their gilded holes of marginalization
We shall leave their gilded holes of racism
We shall leave their gilded holes of white supremacy

Mother
Oh Mother Africa
And we shall drink from your Saharan wells of purity
And we shall visit our childhoods' watersheds of purity
Where gallant lions walk away from barking Trumpists

Mother
We shall abandon the gilded holes of These Parts
The superpowers whose gilded holes entomb misery
Alienation
Dehumanization
Marginalization
Mother, we shall visit the ancient Saharan cosmos
Mother Africa, we shall triumph in our cosmopolitan world

Kwabena O. Akurang-Parry
Accra, Ghana, May 27, 2022

Table of Contents

Table of Contents

Chapter One

Afua took Ko-Ofie's hand. It felt frail in her palms. She glanced at their intertwined fingers. The silver ring that entombed his middle finger was discolored. It looked like the blotches that had come to inhabit her bleached skin.

Afua slowly let go Ko-Ofie's hand.

A searing feeling of brittle weakness registered in his palms. It had a cutting edge like a sand-paper on a sore skin. He looked at his fingers. The blotched parts stood menacingly like an old chain-saw with stained teeth.

Their fingers bore a memorial tribute to bleaching chemical agents of new self-identity and putative white heritage. There are so many of them. We settle for AMBI because its symbolic acronym stands for AFRICANS MAY BE INDOCTRINATED.

The skin is ceaselessly bleached until it acquires a new identity. It is a pernicious color complex. A fetish in itself. Different skin tones of other parts of the body depend on one's enthusiasm to apply AMBI. This in turn also depends on one's damaged psyche and the mentality of having been enslaved, having been made inferior by colonialism, having been neocolonized, and having been uni-directionally globalized. And there are African school systems teaching that the best comes from the West. The primary rhyme of prospective progressive minds in African schools.

It is no longer the underclass, the brainwashed and the benighted masses, who religiously apply AMBI, but also the educated middle class. Ah the most indoctrinated elites do so with a passion of abandonment. The smearing application of AMBI constitutes the misguided African quest for whiteness and wholeness. Yes, the fairer the complexion the better it is in a society that seeks validation from the white world of theseparts. It is a frantic search for fictive attachment to the perceivedsuperior world of these parts, or overseas conceptualized as the Western world, which is the land of naturally bleached people.It is where Africans yearn to be. They call it Aburokyire. These days the Eastern world also has a magnet of its own! Yes, Africans want to go Asian. It is the chop-stick syndrome! A state of perpetual adrift in navigating development with sticks.

AMBI! Its name is rightly so. After extensive application it is known as AFRICANS MAY BE IMPROVED. AMBI erodes away African identity and induces a miragic sense of whiteness.

****

Ko-Ofie pushed his fingers into his side-pockets, and as his eyes met Afua's, he asked, "Don't you like it?"

Afua didn't respond.

Ko-Ofie pulled out his hand from his pocket, and clinically observed his fingers.

On their way to the elevator, Afua held up Ko-Ofie's hand, reexamined his fingers, and looked into Ko-Ofie forlorn eyes.

Suddenly, she disengaged herself, and asked angrily, "What's wrong with you lately? You're not happy, not at all. And it makes me sick, very sick."

Ko-Ofie focused on the staircase leading to the elevator, and replied, "I don't know for sure, but in the world of these parts happiness has escaped us. You are a part of it. And don't tell methat you are free from it all. All of us are affected."

****

The revulsion, the results of Ko-Ofie's visits to Ghana, recurred.His recollections of the encounters with the homegets, those in Africa who benefit materially from the return of velvet seekersfrom these parts, also known as aburokyire, were vivid. His social encounters with several homegets came to mind: their blotched bleached faces, groins, chests and inner legs, nauseatedhim.

Ko-Ofie's eyelids twitched as these images and others ran through his mind. His mouth was invaded by a flood of saliva.It was bitter like bile. This time, he knew his saliva will cascadelike a waterfall. He could not control the over-flowing saliva. Uncontrollably, like a collapsed dam, the saliva over-flooded the precincts of his lips.

Slowly, a nauseating waterfall of saliva drained the corners of Ko-Ofie's mouth. Meandering on his chin and neck, the flood of saliva cascaded onto his chest.

Afua screamed at the sight of the

3

massive lava of saliva that freely drained the bleached-skin furrows on Ko-Ofie's chin.

Breaking the silence, Ko-Ofie asked, "Afua, my dear wife, won't you clean up this mess?"

"Are wives required to do the cleaning? How am I supposed to cope, Ko-Ofie? Those in Ghana think that we are living in a paradise called these parts. But I am in these parts cleaning your putrid saliva. Every Ghanaian should visit these parts to experience our wretched lifestyle."

Afua pulled out a piece of bright, alluring velvet from her handbag and handed it to Ko-Ofie. He held the velvet with some manicured carefulness. He turned the velvet inside out. Then he proceeded to wipe out the nauseating pool of saliva as if the velvet was not meant for that secular duty.

"Afua, you know that none of us is enjoying this dreary life in these parts," Ko-Ofie remarked, as he continued to clean his salivary mess.

"Yes oh in this gilded shithole of these parts," Afua replied.

Simply, we have become the collaborating agents of those who exploit us. Therefore, we fail to tell those back home how we suffer daily in these parts. I wish that none of us had traveled overseas," Ko-Ofie paused and gasped for air.

"Oh, you are breathing too hard again!"

"It would have been good for our nation-building and self-preservation," Ko-Ofie explained, amidst heavy breathing.

"Yes, to put it mildly, we have become

4

collaborating agents of these parts. Life here destroys and kills us individually, results in social death, and collectively ruins Ghana and Africa as a whole," Afua pontificated.

"Don't you think that you've missed something? What did that African Studies professor say on TV?"

"Well, he said that when we come to these parts we are able to acquire some material things to better our miserable conditions. He also claimed that living in these parts helps us to complete the process of Westernization. Can you believe that professor? It's you and the African elites who are the problem."

"Will you stop that? I'm an intellectual and I don't belong to any elite."

"Well, that's your problem! When will you stop your chauvinist, elitist ways with me? You know it. Your Westernized education sold you to these parts long ago. In fact, long, long ago before you came here. We had better not argue!"

****

Ko-Ofie knew it. He knew that Afua didn't enjoy their dreary life and the fact that he had brought her to these parts through marriage. He didn't want to think about it; certainly not after the uncontrollable discharge of saliva.

****

Ko-Ofie had no control over his pent up feelings. The past kept bursting forth like

5

his own saliva. It haunted him. He had started life in Ghana on a very good note. His life in these parts had brought his humanity to a terrain of nothingness. The road ahead was paved with pessimism. And a social death lurked derisively in the horizon of his life.

****

Breaking the silence, Ko-Ofie said, "I'm not the only one who looks at life in these parts through rose-colored spectacles. We were and are many. And many will be born who will develop the same taste buds for these parts. And it will continue for a long, long time. There are millions in Africa who see coming to these parts as the solution to all problems. Wrong. And I say wrong again"

Afua shot back, "That's not all to it. You've deceived yourself and our people. In spite of the deception, you believe that you've to live here, or you would be considered a failure like many others, who in the bottomless pit of haunting frustration, returned home without the prized velvet. You're a self-absorbed velvet seeker."

"Will you stop this nonsense?"

"For once shut up and let me complete what I've to say! Ko-Ofie, I'm educating you and you call it nonsense?"

"You're educating me! Who told you that?"

Afua paused for breath and continued, "Like all velvet seekers, you continue to deceive people in Ghana by telling them about the glorious, even divine life, in these parts. And this dishonesty will continue. Tell them we lead rustic lifestyles in the mega-cities of these parts. We live in gilded shitholes. Even in the shitholes, we are always on the periphery. The mainstream eludes us. We are marginalized everywhere in these parts. Even, the factories and cleaning jobs, the common job sanctuaries for Africans, are currently not available for our taking."

"Stop these long speeches. Yes, I'm a factory worker, so what?"

In a tone of defiance, Afua continued, "That is not good! Your 'so what' explains our inaction. Hence the factory has become the place of salvation for Africans in their desperate and frantic hunt for the velvet. In these parts, the factory is the shrine for your Master's degree in civil engineering. And it has become the final resting place for your Ph.D. in civil engineering. And all you can say is so what?"

Afua paused and suddenly began to laugh, "Ha ha haa, the potato chips factory, where you cut potatoes to be made into potato chips to feed the mouths of these parts, and all you can say is so what? You're not serious, though, you've your Potato Hiring Degree popularly known as Ph.D. to boot.

****

Ko-Ofie's Ph.D. came to mind again. It was his white supervisor who had advised him that he could only get a "decent job" if he was educated in these parts.

The white supervisor, like many of his

7

kind, had something unique about him: he was a high school drop-out, who reveled in bigoted stereotyping of Africa, masked by what he called black or street jokes.

On one occasion, the supervisor set the whole factory laughing. He contended that Africa was once the food capital of Europe, but today Africans are going hungry and becoming emaciated, while Europeans are growing fat to the extent that their flat behinds are even growing bigger.

Uncontrollable laughter followed as white workers, who hardly spoke to the numerous African workers in the factory, except the usual hello or hi, threw themselves into the mirth.

An elderly white man with an unkempt hair responded, "Hey you black people, I thought you guys are here to learn how to be civilized. You know that you can't make here your home. You've got to go back and live in the dark forest. I don't believe that Africa was ever the food capital of Europe," else why are Africans hungry and emaciated.

Laughter seized the workers and a young white man, who was apparently enjoying the events of that afternoon, threw a cigarette packet in the air, and fueled by the mirth, rose from his chair to catch it, but fell down. Some of the onlookers quickly rushed to his aid, as the chorus of laughter continued to occupy the room.

Suddenly, Ko-Ofie stood up. He cleared his throat and drew the attention of his co-workers whose eyes burrowed into his.

Ko-Ofie moved closer to the elderly white

man with the unkempt appearance and focused his attention on him. Breaking into a sonorous voice, Ko-Ofie surveyed his unprepared audience, and then announced, "My name is Ko-Ofie. It means go back home! I'm from Ghana. And I'm what you call black. For your information, I am an African. I don't blame any of you butyour institutions and norms. Why? Your training, socialization, education, and all your institutions foster racial bigotry. Yes my perspectives on you that I cultivated in Ghana before I came here, in many ways, promote your assumed racial superiority. Now I know better. Yes, I know better today. It takes living among you to come to terms with your racial insecurities whichyou have churned out as racial superiority. I know better now. And I wish my people in Africa knew it all.

Ko-Ofie stopped, made a quick turnaround, surveyed his captiveaudience, and facing the supervisor, continued, "Unfortunately, none of you white workers here went beyond high school." You can't even write. Your literacy is about projecting your accent asindispensably supreme. I know better now.

Pausing for effect, Ko-Ofie stirred down the supervisor and continued, "My educational qualifications have never brought any change in my life-style. I wish that I hadn't gone for a Ph.D.degree. It depresses me daily to think that I've a Ph.D. degree and yet do this type of job, cutting potatoes for a living. My Ph.D. degree in civil engineering is from

9

your best university, yet I'm still cutting potatoes. And unlike most of you, I haven't even been promoted to the potato bagging stage yet! You know what I mean."

Pausing and looking around, Ko-Ofie realized that his words were having the desired effects. The white man with the unkempt appearance began to scratch the back of his neck, as his reddened face showed the weight of regret.

Ko-Ofie decided to finish what he wanted to say. After all, some had even thought that he couldn't speak, because he never showed keen interest in the workplace conversations aboutrestaurants, new videos, sex toys, social media, and so on.

"Do you know what you've done to us here?" Ko-Ofie paused again, surveyed his caged audience, and continued, "You've buried us alive! It's another form of slavery. Only that this time we force ourselves to come here to serve you like bullocks. I want to tell you all that your white ambassadors, businessmen,missionaries and educators, your visiting presidents, occupying soldiers, and diplomatic prostitutes, sleep in the darkest of our forests. It's as simple as that and it's because we respect them! And you know what? No you don't. You can never appreciate itbecause of your bigotry. Your likes in Africa jump down to their deaths from the tallest trees; they don't descend carefully with practiced steps like we do. Do you hear me?"

Ko-Ofie left the room. No one followed him, not even his fellowAfricans. He went to the locker room, changed his uniform, and took his bag. Slamming the door as hard as he could, he walked out, cutting through the evening breeze. The summer evening was still warm. Yet, his inside shook.

****

As Ko-Ofie navigated the parking lot, two elderly white women, his co-workers, approached him. He knew one of them very well. She had read Achebe's *Things Fall Apart* and had requestedthat he discussed the book with her. According to her, the booktold the story of the white man's civilizing mission in Africa. For the first time, it occurred to Ko-Ofie that his education had prepared him for mere adaptations to Western institutions and hegemonic ideologies. His education was just a mechanismto equip him to get along with Western dictates. He was convinced, and he had no doubts about it, that his co-worker had made a lofty, but withering analysis of Achebe's book. Butlike many of his generation, he had nothing to offer. In spite ofthe opportunity to educate her about Africa, he found himself equipped with notions of primitive Africa in the garbled hegemonic language of the West. Regrettably, if the co-worker had asked him about Dickens, Lawrence, Hemingway, Elliot, or Steinbach, he could have flawlessly discussed backgrounds, thematic structures and relevance, characterizations, styles, and settings - both time and place.

****

The present situation reminded him about his first Christmas in these parts. A Christian family had invited him to a Christmas dinner. After dinner, they played an interesting family game. The game was one of the presents that surfaced when the noble white male host opened one of the Christmas boxes. The rule of the game was that one picked a question and the next person to his or her right answered it. In the course of the game, his host picked up a question that asked for the initials of T.S. in T.S. Elliot's name.

"Err, Mr. Ko-Ofie, what does the initial T.S. stand for in T.S. Elliot's name?

"It's Thomas Stearns. That's Thomas Stearns Elliot."

"Why, did you see the answer?" The host interrogated.

Ko-Ofie had taken delight in the host's shocking question! He was prepared to tell the host that T.S. Elliot was one of the Western writers he had studied in high school. But, the host was not amused and directed his attention to the white guests and said, "Make sure the chap sitting next to you doesn't see the answers."

In the course of the game, three of the guests could not answer a question that required listing four of Hemingway's books. When it came to Ko-Ofie's turn, he smiled, and rattled off four titles of Hemingway's books, the last of which was *A Farewell to Arms*.

The host shifted a little in his chair, and asking no one in particular, said, "Am I sitting in the comfort of my own home this

Christmas night?"

When no one volunteered an answer, the host focused on Ko-Ofie and almost foaming at the mouth, stated, "That's interesting, very interesting indeed! Can you please tell us what that book is all about, I mean *A Farewell to Arms*?"

Ko-Ofie thoroughly discussed the book, cited quotations to back his illuminations, and discussed its stylistic dignities and infelicities.

"Shaking his head, the host asked, "Did the hero return to America?"

"No, he didn't," replied Ko-Ofie.

Looking contented, the host retorted, "I thought as much; I knew you were telling lies all along. Anyway, I don't intend tospoil the best dinner of your life; your answers have been goodguesses."

Ko-Ofie had wanted to challenge the host's peroration, but the white guests' profuse laughter drowned his enthusiasm.

These and other images are common now. Each situation recalled a set of memory that only served to reawaken bitter lived-experiences in these parts.

****

Smiles lit the face of the two co-workers. Both approached Ko- Ofie. And one of them said, "Hi there, we're here to tell you how sorry we're. I mean all of us."

"No, don't bother," Ko-Ofie replied calmly.

Then another set of memory came into

focus. Such apologies and smiles meant nothing to him. Not anymore. They were manufactured smiles subtly unfurled to appease him.

The co-worker who spoke moments ago pleadingly asked, "Areyou going home now? Please, can you give us a ride?"

Knowing that it was their way of making amends, Ko-Ofie asked, "Why a ride today of all days?" "We only want a ride, and nothing more.""Where are your cars?"

"Our mechanics have them! Hey we're only asking you to give
us a ride; nothing more."

In order to diffuse the mounting tension, the other co-worker asked, "What is the name of the man with the unkempt appearance?"

"I don't know, I've never bothered to find out. That man is an asshole," the co-worker who had spoken earlier replied.

Ko-Ofie asked them, "So, do you know my name?"

"Yeah, we know your name. You just told us. I guess we didn't.I guess I should say I didn't."

"So what name did you use for me then?"

"Well, we sometimes called you the black guy or the African man."

"I know all your names. Yes, everyone. You are Linda andthis is Marsha. Where I come from names are very important.It does not only identify a person; it shows love. A name is a human fortress by itself. How can you work with people for seven years without knowing their names?"

14

The two co-workers smiled; Marsha brushed a lock of hair from her forehead, and politely asked, "Why're you telling us all these?"

"Why are you smiling or laughing? Am I so vulnerable in whatever I do and say? To you what I had said was a speech from an exotic beast that is out to impress his superiors," Ko- Ofie uttered.

****

A voice from the hurt within asked Ko-Ofie to stop, but he knew he had to continue, "I know I'm not making any sense to you at all. You've your biased ideas. They're fixed from childhood. As infants, you're tutored by the socialization machine you call television. And then there are the vectors of racism you learn in schools, starting right from kindergarten."

Realizing that the two co-workers were mesmerized and even shocked, Ko-Ofie paused, took in a deep breath, and continued, "It's not only the young," he stressed, pointed at the two co-workers, and continued, "but warped images are fed to adults, until their deaths. But even in death the images go on. You know what I mean, I bet you do!" Ko-Ofie paused for an answer.

Discerning, that no answer was forthcoming, he continued "White represents a blissful Heaven and black the dreadful hell."

"Excuse me! We didn't come here to quarrel with you. We only asked for a ride. Please be patient with us. Don't think all whitesare the same, for we're not, just as all blacks aren't the same," Linda pleadingly proclaimed.

"I'm sorry. May be I got carried away. But it was about time I spoke my mind. Let us go then."

****

But the images of what Ko-Ofie had wanted to say foughtin his mind. It was as if he had been programed to make a proclamation to the world. They were images that marginalizedand denigrated Africans in these parts.

****

As these thoughts plowed through Ko-Ofie's mind, his two co-workers kept laughing and happily clapped intermittently. Then it dawned on Ko-Ofie that it was better if he abandoned his own insularity and parochialism.

The two co-workers had come to make amends, but none spoketo him on the way home. It was not until Marsha alightedthat Linda said, "I never knew you could speak so well. I was impressed today by what you told that asshole of a man. Ko- Ofie, I'm really sorry. I mean it. All of us are sorry, you know, we felt really bad. It's strange to me! I hope you understand. I mean that man's crude behavior is appalling."

"Linda, it is okay with me. Thanks for your concern.""Eh," Linda intoned, "Please,

I will get down here." "But this is no safe place to get down."

"We only joined you because we were moved by what you had said. Thanks. We'll see you next week. Have a nice weekend."

****

Alone and on his way home, Ko-Ofie thought about several things. The supervisor's words, what he had said to the man with the unkempt appearance, and the reaction of Marsha and Linda. Finally what his supervisor had previously said about a "decent job" had a meaning. After all, he cut potatoes for eighthours per day in a decent factory with arthritic elderly white women. These women readily smiled at him every morning, followed by the usual "How is the weather?" He even knew thehour and whose turn it was to ask about the weather. At least, the work was decent, and he was working with arthritic elderlywhite women who tolerated him.

Ko-Ofie took a look at the driving mirror, and remarked to himself, "Well, at any rate, I'm better off than many Africans in these parts!"

****

Many Africans work in smoke-filled factories and dingy bars. And blessed are many who are cleaners of the night, late into thenight. There are also cleaners of old white body parts. Oh private emaciated parts!

17

Cleaning is a special profession reserved for Africans, mostly those whose visas to these parts have expired, or lack "papers." The body cleaners are euphemistically called live-in nurses. And it is a silent joke among Africans, indeed, an obscure joke that turns out to be rather prophetic: Africans work seven months in these parts and return to Africa seventy-seven years dead!

****

Adjusting the driving mirror, Ko-Ofie looked at himself for a long time. Suddenly, a car horn jolted him into reality.

****

Alongside the road, prostitutes were selling their wares. Ko- Ofie had seen them too often, mostly African women. But that is a small part of the story: it is not only African women who are prostituting their bodies in these parts, but also African men. Hmm! The African male prostitutes with their bleached skin tones! Ah! Their variegated complexions radiate in the conspiring neon lights of these parts, casting shadows of contorted images on forbidden, sanguinary streets. And their peroxide-induced permed flamboyant wavy hairdos flyin opposite directions as they chase after the soliciting cars of white men, lusting after blackness.

All these Africans! Yes, they are Africa's young and virile. They are the heroes and heroines of contemporary Africa. They are the role models. But then, there is a footnote to it: those young andvirile African prostitutes were once children. Their collective ambition was to travel across the jaded Sahara, complaisant Mediterranean, and tortuous middle-passaged Atlantic, plangent Indian Ocean, and the pliable Pacific. These are the routes of the velvet seekers, who return to their places of birth in Africa, seventy-seven years living dead. They are consecrated "being-tos." Shrines and monuments are erected in their honor in Africa even after they have wasted away in these parts.

****

It is a costly dream, yet velvet seekers cannot afford to be so critical. The residual effects of the velvet affect every African.It is all about the search for the velvet. The velvet ultimately leads to the search for the cargoes of these parts. And that is thedream of Africans. The significant cargo is a used car.

Yet, the true story is never told to those in Africa. That would amount to the ritual demolition of the shrine and monuments reserved for the velvet seekers. It would exacerbate the painfuldeath of those who are already seventy-seven years dead.

****

The thought of the velvet increased the saliva oozing from Ko-Ofie's mouth.

Continuing its outward journey, the saliva activated a tense uneasiness in his body.

"What's this? What's this saliva for? It's not even saliva any more. It's mucous of some sort. You're so quiet these days! What is going through your mind? You're totally alienated from me. Anyway, hurry to the washroom to clean up," Afua lamented and instructed.

"It is the thought of the velvet and nothing more," Ko-Ofie replied, as he made what at that moment appeared a long journey to the washroom.

****

Many people were waiting for the elevator that had anchored on the 19th floor, to come down. It didn't take Ko-Ofie that long. He came back before the elevator berthed on the ground floor. As Ko-Ofie veered towards Afua, some of the people waiting for the elevator gazed at him.

****

Suddenly, a white man in a wheel chair suffered a seizure. Simultaneously, a young white woman, who was holding tenaciously onto two metal walking sticks screamed. She had weaknesses in both legs. There was a big bulge, like a pillow, that extended from her chest down to the region of her stomach. The two walking sticks were in her left hand, while her right hand was glued across her chest in an apparent effort to reduce the sagging weight of whatever was stored on her chest.

She released her right hand to wipe off a stream of phlegm from her nose. It was then that the onlookers realized that the bulging weight was nothing, but her breast! The left breast was longer and bigger than the right breast. The pitiful owner took hold of the left breast and moved towards the elevator door as it opened.

****

Following in Afua's footsteps, Ko-Ofie stole a glance at the white girl with the gigantic, ponderous breast, and began the journey to the elevator.

As Ko-Ofie approached Afua, she whispered to him, "It's only when you come to these parts that you learn that strange diseaseshave a home here. If you're in Africa, you're programmed to think that these parts are all a disease-free paradise."

Afua and Ko-Ofie were the last to join the elevator.

In a practiced way, the young white woman with the ponderous breasts, wiped off a stream of congested phlegm from thecorners of her nose, causing her left breast again to come out ofits secret hiding.

Instantly, a young white boy of about ten years old began to lick his lips. Making some carnal noises, the young white boy inserted his middle finger into his mouth and began to slip it inand out his pouted lips.

****

The elevator door opened on the 4th floor and the white man in the wheelchair gave way to the woman with the ponderous breast to exit.

Anchoring the two metal walking sticks on the floor of the elevator, the young white woman with the ponderous breast shouted, "I hate to be in this elevator with black people." She paused and wiped off a jagged mountain of phlegm from the corners of her mouth. After that she pointed at Ko-Ofie, and said, "Especially, you who smells like vomit and shit. Next time make sure you take the stairs. This is not an African enclave of a shithole for diseased people."

A momentary, shocking silence followed. It was broken by an unsolicited laughter from an elderly black man, whose neck was bedecked with what looked like a set of gold-embroidered dog chains. The elderly black man held the elevator door open for those who were exiting.

Looking very contended, the black man surveyed Afua and Ko-Ofie and calmly stated that "You Africans are disgusting. Did you hear that white lady? Did you hear her statement?"

Afua calmly replied, "And what are you? Are you the most stupid black man that ever lived?"

Angered by Afua's repartee, the elderly black man released his hold on the elevator door. As a result, the elevator door hit the wheelchair of the white man who had the seizure, throwing him back into the elevator.

Abruptly, the elevator door closed and

started its upward journey.

Then the white man who had the seizure screamed, "I don't want to be with you sick Africans; you're all diseased, deformed, maimed, sick and sickening. Fuck you all."

The elderly black man looked derisively at Ko-Ofie and Afua and then smiled at the white man who had the seizure. Parading a grin that even brightened the metal components of his bedecked necklace, the elderly black man in a placating mood said to the white man who had the seizure, "I'm sorry, you see, they're Africans."

With a practiced hand, the white man who had the seizure tookhold of the arm of his wheelchair, and as if he was in a great mental pain, replied, "And you, where do you think you come from? You think you're white! For your information you're also black, a color, not even an African. You're one and the same people. You're an African. You should've learnt that long ago. It doesn't matter whether you're born here, USA, or the Caribbean, or Britain, fundamentally, you ought to trace your descent to Africa. Your homeland is Africa."

The white man who had the seizure moved his wheelchair in order to face the elderly black man, and the latter smiled as if he knew the former. But the white man who had the seizure didn't return the smile, but continued, "And if you go home tonight repair that surgical intonation of yours and discard thatstrained accent. For it is neither American nor Caribbean. Be yourself and stop the stupid imitation of accents"

The elderly black man frowned and replied, "Oh, yes, I'm black, but not an African. I come from the Caribbean and it's nearer to you than Africa. That's the difference. And that's what makes us, the Caribbean people, more civilized than Africans, who are further away from you. Besides, we've allowed you to turn our beaches into your entertainment backyards. Therefore, we share a common bond and cultural proximity. "

The elderly black man paused and when he realized that no response was forthcoming perorated, "It's a simple mathematical model: the nearer you're to America, I mean the US of A, the more civilized you're. Brilliant! Oh! Brilliant!"

The white man who had the seizure edged close to the elevatordoor. As he did so, the elderly black man was forced to move to where Afua and Ko-Ofie were standing.

Afua smiled wryly and addressed the elderly black man, "White man from the Caribbean, our knight of the Caribbean, it's unfortunate that you've been told by your co-equal in all things that you're a person of African descent. I pity you. Howold are you? Sixty plus! And you've had to wait that long to betold that you've African roots? You must have experienced thatpain in your life!"

Afua bent down a little to make sure that the white man had theseizure could hear her, and continued, "Thank you very much. You're the most sincere white person I've ever met. For once you didn't pit continental Africans against Diasporic Africans.!"

Then, Afua turned to address the elderly

black man, "Andyou my white prince, I
hope you and your kind learn fromthis.
Aping of whites has brought us nothing but
misery and ridicule."

****

The elevator door opened. They were now
on the sixth floor. The white man who had
the seizure exited, followed by the elderly
black man.

****

Laughing, Afua retorted "This elderly
black man, oh, Ko-Ofie, I understand why
you vomit!"

"Afua, I don't know anymore. What can I
say? The velvet is sickening. But it's also true
that its brightest parts are alluring,"lamented
Ko-Ofie.

Afua replied, "Ko-Ofie, Africans will
remain marginalized in these parts forever. It
is an unsettling, strange pessimism. Evenlook
at the racism that African football players on
the proverbial equal playing fields suffer in
Europe."

****

But Ko-Ofie didn't answer immediately.
He reflected on the rude white man at the
factory, the white woman with theponderous
breast, the wheel-chair bound white man, and
the elderly black Caribbean man.

****

Ko-Ofie then took in a deep breath and commented, "You know, Afua, every non-African looks down upon Africans. Why is it so?"

"Oh, to be an African in these parts, you mean? Those at home will never know our horrible experiences of tribulations and pain in these parts! It's a journey to a living death," responded Afua.

****

The elevator stopped on the twelfth floor and a white couple joined them. The white woman pressed on the 17th-floor button. Suddenly, she shrieked at the sight of the phlegm-layered finger marks of the white woman with the ponderous breast that had been imprinted on the wall of the elevator.

The white woman's periodic look at Afua was broken when the elevator jerked as it stopped on the fifteenth floor for a group of white kids to join.

Hoping to prevent the white boys from touching the phlegm- layered finger print, the white woman intoned, "You kids watch that thing on the wall. Shit, it looks like menstrual blood! Let us leave this damned elevator and take the stairs; it is only two flights up anyway. Shit, I know that black people can do bad things, but this is fucking shit. I can't believe that they do that in a public elevator! Look, the black woman is in her bloody period? Shit, these people can do strange things! Were

26

they fucking in the elevator too? My, oh my! These primitive savages are now here to destroy everything, even elevator walls!"

As the white woman and her companion strutted out of the elevator, she boldly shouted at Afua, "Bitch! Who else could've plastered these white walls with this damn blackish, smelling thing? Only black people can do that fucking thing and fuck in an elevator!"

Afua held the elevator door open and shouted back, "You bitch of all bitches, now I know how sick you are. I'm not in Africa where people think that whites are angels. I live here with you, bitch. It is your fucking kind who besmeared the wall with what your fucking men like to eat."

****

The elevator door opened to a dark and ominous corridor. Afua and Ko-Ofie followed their known steps. Afua opened the door. She walked to the window and took in a deep breath. She stood there for a long time. Her face and thoughts were trapped by polluted air that invaded the room through the window sills.

****

Ko-Ofie sat in a chair at the far corner of the room. He was oblivious to the world of these parts. The last vestiges of the saliva drained the corners of his mouth.

Afua turned around and looked at him for

a long time. Then, she turned again to face the world of these parts through the ominous window. And as she walked away into the bedroom of their living death, she glanced once more at Ko-Ofie, and whispered, "The velvet seekers."

Chapter Two

Ko-Ofie looked at his gilded-embroidered wall-clock. And he remembered all about it. The time spent in these parts was withering.

****

The search for the velvet has another norm to it: struggling Africans in these parts don't tell those in Africa about their sufferings and tribulations! Anyone who does that betrays the collective dream. It aborts the collective African dream. The dream is about crusading for the cargo cult of these parts. The velvet is entirely anything foreign, but African.

****

Ko-Ofie turned around and looked at their material things, including fridges, VCRs, TV sets, I-pads, cellphones, and pianos. These are the indictors, which in the parlance of the velvet seekers, points to the fact that he has achieved it all in these parts. Smiling to himself, Ko-Ofie intoned, "Are these gadgets our new ways, our new norms, our new ideologies, and our hope for the present and the future of Africa!"

****

The gadgets are symbols of wealth! They also symbolize the whiteness that velvet seekers hope to acquire. The first fruition of the cargo-cult mentality, constructed around the velvet, occurs before the first return visit to Africa. Once the velvet is acquired, it speaks to the idea that they have really arrived in the hallowed precincts of the cargo-cult mentality of these parts.

****

Velvet seekers, who return to Africa without the cargo, substitute harrowing stories to preface their failure to acquire the velvet, the pristine symbol of the cargo- cult mentality. The velvet seekers who fail are often given derogatory names. The become subjects of communal jokes and popular derision.

****

Ko-Ofie closed his eyes. In the ensuing darkness of his mind, he began to speak aloud, "But this immemorial Africa. The noble savage Africa. Africa that has no history. Africa that has not contributed to the civilization of the world. These and others are being replayed in many forms to denigrate Africans. That's why we Africans shouldn't leave Africa, shouldn't desert our land in search of material wealth in these parts. Africans should search for their material souls in Africa, not in these parts. That day will be the beginning of plenty to come. Oh! My pain and this alienation will undo me."

Touching his head with his left fingers,

Ko-Ofie swept away sweat on his forehead. He sat straight-up, folded his arms on his chest, and continued, "Afua thinks that I'm sick. I'm not. Not at all! It's the pangs of pain that make my thoughts wander off. Ha! Did they say I make big issues out of small issues? Ah! The civilization of these parts! The murders, rapes, abductions, incest, democracy for the rich and whites, violence for comic relief, and guns for hire in the realms of sanitized narratives are elements of what people of these parts see as the pinnacle of their civilization. And yes, these are carefully deodorized when questioning the causes that lead to such deviant behaviors and atrocious violence."

"Ko-Ofie, it's too early to rant. Come here, at least, come and watch TV with me," Afua suggested.

Entering the living room, Ko-Ofie commented, "You watch all these images. Anyway, what you're watching is good. At least they're white images of themselves. They're urbane and sanitized."

Afua went and sat by Ko-Ofie, extended her arms, took his hand, and placed him beside her like a child. She gently put her arms around him, and said, "Sure, you know, propaganda is a perfected art in these parts, especially the craft of dehumanizing and demonizing Africans."

"Yes, I know," replied Ko-Ofie, as he nudged closer to Afua, "The presentation of Africa is too bad by any standards. Those TV images of Africans are all exaggerations. We know that they are falsified, exaggerated

31

images that deal with suffering, emaciation, and living death in Africa."

Ko-Ofie cleared his throat for a long monologue, "Yeah, after all, in these parts there are hungry, emaciated people whowill never be seen by the people of Africa. In these parts, there are millions of hungry people cloying to death. In these parts, hungry people are chained to decaying walls, forlorn alleys, deserted parks, haunting shopping malls, and sanguinary parking lots, all dehumanized hubs of their civilization. Such bereft and demented souls will never be known to or seen by the people of Africa.

Afua, caressed Ko-Ofie's hand, and said, "Ko-Ofie, relax. You are making your condition worse by these suffusing and devastating thoughts.

But Ko-Ofie, as if oblivious of what Afua was doing, continued, "What Africans at home know is the "HOLLYwudization" of neon lights that points to fulfillment and beauty, not deprivation,suffering and hunger in these parts. And what Africans learn about these parts deal with CNNNization that sanitizes crimes, racism, global hegemony, political corruption, Conversely, CNNN would have considered such in Africa as immemorial and decadent, in fact, timeworn behaviors of Africans that the White Man's Burden and Civilizing Mission of European colonization, Christianity, and civilized-driven Globalization couldn't change for the better.

"Ko-Ofie, stop all these."

Ko-Ofie paused and continued, "I'll be

pleased to do that at a later date.

Afua impatiently replied, "When oh when?"

Please, for now listen to me, Ko-Ofie continued, "I'm saying that Africans will always be fed on the crumbs that fall from the tables of the people of these parts. These crumbs are a refuse heap and the owners have nothing to lose. But the crumbs have a tincture of their owners' saliva: once eaten, the recipients forever have the craving of the owners of the crumbs."

"Oh, now, you're speaking in tongues!" remarked Afua, as sheclapped, laughed, and asked, "So who are the recipients here?"

"We're the recipients. And we're the velvet seekers. We've directcontacts with the owners of the velvet cargo. The people of theseparts control the crumbs that have led to our dependency."

"So why do we eat the crumbs?"

"Because we are powerless and had been conditioned to accept their taste."

"What about the modern satellite dishes that broadcast the neon images of these parts to Africa? Don't you think these have effects on our tastes?"

In an impatient tone, Ko-Ofie continued, "Let me finish what I've to say. You've a point there, though. I believe that we the velvet seekers should accept part of the blame."

"But the people of these parts promote the cargo cult mentality of satellites of corrupted movies, propaganda magazines, racistAfricanists, and what have you!"

"What about us? I mean all of us, the velvet seekers, and even African governments and families receiving our remittances and so on? Of course, this is a complex issue. African governments may not be able to stop velvet seekers from coming to these parts. But it's the misrule of African governments that brings Africans to these parts. I mean things like magazines, movies, and educational materials can be controlled to some extent."

In a paradoxical twist, Ko-Ofie cleared his throat and said, "What oh and what can we do?"

"Afua calmly replied, "Well, you gave up hope long ago. As a result, we shall continue to depend on the crumbs of these parts and also see these parts as the citadel of civilization, science and technology."

"So what do you mean by civilization, science, and technology?""Ha, but you are an engineer! Well, for me civilization is a way of life for any people. Every society has science, hence science is universal. Technology is the way that people relate to their environment. And I think Africans can borrow from other places. But it shouldn't be a wholesale acceptance of the values of others. We've lost track of our own needs and how to fulfill them ourselves."

"Hmm, so that's your definition of science and technology!"

"You thought I was going to define them in your terms, the way these parts have trained you to think. The time has come for us to question some concepts, paradigms, and theories that have been imposed on us since our contact with Europe."

Ko-Ofie laughed, but quickly recollected himself, and said, "That's true. You're right, very right. We know so much about all these things that affect us! Why can't we change the situation?

Afua replied, "It's a cycle in which we Africans have come to accept the cultural habits of the oppressor. And the oppressors know that we are too eager to accept them. My answer is that until we embark on a cultural revolution on our own terms, that pernicious cycle will continue, no matter what we know or how often we lament."

Ko-Ofie got up, and began to pace back and forth.

"If you want to march like a soldier, please, go and look for another room, better still, an open field."

As Ko-Ofie walked into the bedroom, he saw the steeple of a church building in the distance through the window.

Turning to Afua, Ko-Ofie exclaimed, "The church, the church, oh the church!"

"Ko-Ofie, please, don't! Please not now! If you talk about the church, I will be forced to go to the park and leave you here by yourself. Go to the bedroom," Afua pleaded.

****

Ko-Ofie remembered it all. The white priest had used the whole morning sermon to detail hunger and material deprivations in Africa. The priest, Reverend White Warr, exhibited remarkable intensity of vigor and enthusiasm. It was such that Rev. Warr sweated profusely, despite the spring morning and the airy comfort provided by the air condition in the room. Rev. Warr elaborated and amplified his instructive sermon with PowerPoint slides that exaggerated appalling poverty, acidic hunger, gangrened emaciated bodies, and the dearth of African inventiveness.

Rev. Warr pranced from one end of the pulpit to another. Occasionally, he laughed when horrifying scenes appeared on the screen. It was as if he wanted to soothe the fears of the congregation. Rev. Warr wiped away sweat that had irrigated his broad Victorian forehead with a white handkerchief. As he pranced about and whirled the wet white handkerchief, more sweat drained his sacred bald head.

"Let us all sing `Rescue the Perishing,' Rev Warr implored the almost all white congregation."

Ko-Ofie shifted a little in his seat in response to Rev. Warr's whirling of the white handkerchief.

A white woman with a pony tail, who was sitting next to Ko- Ofie, eyed him. When their eyes met the second time, she smiled at him, barring all her thirty-two teeth like a dog would at someone it had seen so often, yet could not identify at all.

Rev. Warr continued to twirl the white handkerchief around his head and intoned, "Rescue the dying," and the white congregation offered the refrain, "For we're merciful and we'll save them."

The images continued on the screen. All the images of doom, bright, telling, vivid, very penetrating, and the best that the modern digital camera could conjure, appeared. The colors of the images were twilight-like. The cinematic images figuratively pried into abnormal African bones, inspected African tumors, examined African intestinal worms, weighed African nasal phlegm, and surveyed African tubercular sores.

The white congregation punctuated these images with sighs, tears, and groans.

Then, the majestic houseflies of Africa arrived on the cinematicscreen, frolicking in hollow living eye sockets of children and the aged, all long lost to hunger and emaciation.

Besieging the screen and eclipsing the houseflies, dark images of sprouting, squeaking squadrons of vultures hovered over children that were too emaciated and weak to defend themselves.

Ko-Ofie closed his eyes to the confrontational images on the screen.

Suddenly, a white boy's screams pierced the murmuring chorus of the congregation. Momentarily his screams stifled thecollective concentration on the graphic cinematic images of theAfrican doom.

The white boy looked at the direction of Ko-Ofie and pointed at him. A white man beside the white boy, presumably his father, held the white boy's hand and pointed it at the screen. In spite of his father's efforts to calm him down, the white boy screamed harder than before.

Ko-Ofie bowed his head, as piercing eyes focused on his direction, indicating that he was the cause of the boy's discomfort.

Focusing on where the white boy sat, the priest's sonorous voice rose with a new song, "Blest be the tie that binds us to Jesus' love," and the congregation joined in.

It was not the finality of Rev. Warr's sermon, but the conclusion of the film that was imprinted on Ko-Ofie's mind. Rev. Warr had asked for offerings to be given to the suffering Africans, and as the congregation sang, the cinematic scene shifted and focused on an African boy, who stood gallantly behind a cache of guns.

The African boy's body was clothed in rounds of ammunition with bright manufacturers' tags that read "Made in U.S.A.," "Made in France," "Made in Germany," and one appeared with the Union Jack. Then "Made in U.S.S.R.," "Pruned in South Africa", "With Contribution from Sweden," With Consent From the Other African Countries," and "Your Neighbors the Africans, Agreed."

Then, the African boy pointed the gun to the south and began to shoot.

As the shots rang out, the cinematic scene shifted onto African women and children in a file, carrying all their possessions in gun and ammunition paper boxes. They were followed by men herding animals.

Again the African boy adorned with ammunition labels gave some warning shots and uttered a loud and ear-shattering noise. Instantly, about fifty African men dressed in military fatigues and bearing weapons emerged from a nearby thicket. Behind the African men of war were two whites, a man and a woman. They had the same guns which the African boy had used to firethe warning shots.

The African men of war wore large identification tags in various colors with several visible writings on them, including:

I AM A SOLDIER TRAINED FOR COUPS; TRAINED TO RAPE OUR WOMEN, AND TRAINED TO KILL MY FELLOW CITIZENS.

I AM AN INDUSTRIAL & FOOD SCIENTIST - MS.C. (EUROPA)AND PH.D. (AMERICUS), TRAINED TO APPROVE THE IMPORTATION OF POISONED FOOD FOR MY PEOPLE.

I AM THE MINISTER OF FINANCE AND ECONOMIC PLANNING, TRAINED TO PLACE MY PERSONAL ECONOMICNEEDS FIRST. THE POCKETS OF MY FAMILY ARE FULL OF GOLD BARS THAT WILL BE DEPOSITED IN FOREIGN BANKS.

I AM THE MINISTER OF TRANSPORTATION AND PETROLEUMPRODUCTS WHO SUPPLY PETROLUEM PRODUCTS TO MY PERSONAL 22 CARS, 22 COMMERCIAL BUSES, AND 22 CARS FOR MY GIRLFRIENDS. I IMPORT UNSUITABLE CARSFOR MY GOVERNMENT SO LONG AS THOSE

FOREIGN MANUFACTURERS GIVE
MY TEN PERCENT BRIBES.

I AM THE MINISTER OF HEALTH -
DIP. SURVEYING (LONDONUS
POLYTECHNICUS), TRAINED TO
FURNISH MANUFACTURED DATA
ON DISEASES IN MY COUNTRY TO
FOREIGN ARM-CHAIR
RESEARCHERS. AND OH, I GET TO
TRAVEL AND GET PAID. AGAIN
FOREIGN SCIENTISTS ARE MY
SOURCES OF WEALTH. I OFFER
BOGUS STATISTICS AND OTHER
INFORMATION ON MY COUNTRY'S
HEALTHCARE TOTHEM AND THEY
GIVE ME DOLLARS IN RETURN.

I AM MINISTER OF TOURISM - B.A.
(NEW YORKUS), TRAINED TO LURE
ECONOMIC AND CULTURAL
PROSTITUTES INTO MYCOUNTRY.

As the marching African men of war
initiated a turn on the path, the tags faded
away.

Far in the distance, suddenly, the African
men of war stopped.

The white man stood in front of them,
removed his shirt and put on a new shirt with
several writings, some of which read:

REPRESENTING AMMUNITION
BENEVOLENCESENT BY THE BANK
OF THE WORLD
SENT TO SAP ECONOMIC AND
STRUCTURAL PLANS

SENT BY SECOND-HAND OR
USED GOODS COMPANIES TO
INCREASE YOUR WESTERN TASTE
REPRESENTING UNSCRUPULOUS
FOREIGN MEDICALSCIENTISTS
REPRESENTING THE WHITE
MEDIA PEOPLE WHO RECREATE
IMMEMORIAL AFRICA

The white man swayed as if he was conducting a Victorian orchestra. He raised his hands. And the voices of African men of war, echoed his message in a song:

> We are marching to somewhere To somewhere, nowhere, where We shall kill them, our neighbors As we have been given new guns With our new guns, new ideology
> With our new guns, marching, killing Marching, maiming, devastating the land Our new guns from the civilized world From the civilized, humane world Marching, killing, maiming, burning And happily devastating our lands

The song came to an end and the white man proclaimed, "Theseguns are important in our new bilateral relationship. They're a protective mechanism against conquest by neighboring countries. These weapons will prevent you from being dominated by other ethnic groups."

The white woman stepped forward, faced southwards, raised her gun, discharged some bullets into space, and proclaimed, "These are our seeds. They will always germinate in the South. They're a part of the new world order."

****

Ko-Ofie's concentration on the screen was broken by the priest's peroration, "In the name of our Lord God above, let us save them. These African souls made wretched by their own designsand complicity."

****

Ko-Ofie understood the meaning of the relationship between the words of the white woman and the priest's peroration.Both are common themes that are found on TV all the time. Every viewer in these parts, whether black or white, knows that Africans suffer from diseases and live daily in unfettered clawsof immemorial Africa-made poverty.

****

There was every indication that the white congregation had felt the impact of the sermon: they applauded with Amen, Amen.

****

Looking around, Ko-Ofie's focus fell on a black child standing near a bearded black man.

As the curtain fell on the screen, the black child pointed at it and screamed, "Who were all those suffering black people?"

The black child stood there for some time. He appeared lost in the throngs of people exiting the church. He moved toward a painting of a bearded white man on the wall. The bearded white man appeared to be holding a long stick with some animals in front of him.

As the black child turned to face the other side of the room, his eyes confronted those of the bearded black man, and the latter said meekly, "My son, please come and be with me."

The black child didn't respond, but continued walking toward the painting of the bearded white man on the wall.

Ko-Ofie's gaze met that of the bearded black man. And both simultaneously looked at the black child as he stood before the massive painting, caressing it with a smile that had long left their time-worn faces.

Suddenly, the black child screamed, "Daddy, Daaady, when are you gonna tell me about those black people in the film? Why are they so thin and sick?"

A white woman on her way out of the church knelt beside the black child. Slowly and methodically, she raised him up as if for a better aerial viewing. Then she planted him comfortably beside the bearded black man, smiled, began to walk away, andthen turned around to look at both, and announced, "They're Africans just like you! They're your people. Lucky you! Lucky you, indeed, lucky you to be living here! Lucky you to see the sad experience of poverty in Africa in a documentary film here,instead of living it out there in Africa!"

The white woman's peroration stuck in Ko-Ofie's mind. But he was jolted into reality, by an African lady who was roaming about in the church. She had the forlorn languidness of an actress long lost in her dramatic role. Tucking up her massive dress, the African lady approached the black child.

****

Ko-Ofie had seen the grotesque appearance of the African lady somewhere: her dress bore a resemblance to a picture in his mind's eye. It was long ago. He pursed his lips in a little smile: the umbrella-like dress resembled one worn by the Queen of England on a plaque plastered on a wall of his former primary school. The plaque was saluted by pupils as a part of the rituals of the morning assembly of students. Every morning, all the pupils waited for Dr. A.E.Q. to talk about the virtues conferred on them by the British Empire. Dr. A.E.Q. stands for Alfred Edward Quark. His surname was Ever-Fullson. It was said that his real name was Kwaku Kani, but he changed it during his studies at Oxford.

Dr. A.E.Q. was the only person in the town with a doctorate degree. The whole town believed that he was an enigma. It was said that he drank only from a cup engraved with the Union Jack. He spoke the Queen's English through his nasal cavity. As a result, he was also known as the Dr. Nose Speaker. Townspeople wondered why he alone didn't use his mouth, but his nose as a vessel of speech.

There were many stories about Dr. A. E. Q. It was said thathe was never interested in the indigenous Odwira Festival, claiming that he could not have communion with African ancestors, because the dead had no meaning in his view. But it was also said that Dr. A. E. Q's academic specialization was the death of the key leaders of the British Empire and the demise of the soul of the British Empire. And he attended local funerals always swinging an umbrella embossed with the Union Jack. At such funerals, he was heard mourning the passing away of the ruling elites of the British Empire. He always wore a suitof white coat and a pair of blue trousers. He was the ultimate modern Ghanaian scholar with the enviable title of M.B.E.

****

Smiling, the African lady said, "Hi I'm Eve from Kenya. Where are ya from? Ghana?

Ko-Ofie looked at her closer, smiled and said, "Yes, I'm from Ghana. How did you know?"

"I can always tell the country of origin of Africans I meet. Ya Ghanaians and Nigerians are identified with ya traditional fashion-statements. We Kenyans also dress flamboyantly, but with an indication that the British presence is still with us in the Serengeti."

Ko-Ofie smiled and the African lady returned his smile, and said, "I'm very sorry, I haven't spoken to someone in a long time. Ya know, I like talking, but here I don't get the chance to speak with people. Have ya met my husband yet?"

The African lady turned her gaze toward the left side of Ko-Ofieand smiled wryly. Ko-Ofie also turned around and realized thather husband was the bearded African man who was still gluedto an arm-chair with his face in his palms.

The African lady focused on Ko-Ofie and said, "Ya never told me ya name."

"Oh! I'm sorry, I'm Ko-Ofie. Err, is that your husband over there?"

"Yes, is something the wrong?"

"Oh! No! I saw him during the service, and I said to myself he must be an African," replied Ko-Ofie.

****

Ko-Ofie noticed something that the African lady had in common with most Africans that he had met in these parts: they gave the impression of having mastered the accents of white people of these parts. And, they did so proudly. But once they spoke for a length of time, their imitated, counterfeit Anglo-Saxon accents would desert them like the sun parting company with the approaching darkness. Ko-Ofie knew they would ask you about when you arrived in these parts. But it had nothing todo with your welfare. If your riddled answer indicated

46

that you just arrived, it became a triumph for them: they were more acquainted with the intricacies of these parts and were happy in their belief that they had acquired more velvets than the newly arrived.

****

The embroidered clock chimed. Ko-Ofie raised his head to look at it. It was five o'clock.

Ko-Ofie whispered to himself, "Yes, I need a better time table in my life than this clock is willing to tell me."

Afua heard the whisper and asked, "What's it now with you?"

"Oh! The clock informed me about the time I've spent in these parts."

"Are you getting crazy again? How can a clock tell you about your life here? Get up and do something with your life. You don't even chat with me anymore, except for those meaningless ramblings. I'm also fed up. You're not the only one suffering in these parts. I am too. All of us are!"

****

Ko-Ofie turned and faced the window once more. It was difficult for him to look far into the distance. Yet, he could see a mass of smoke of various shades and colors emanating from different factories. Snaking across the sky, the edges of the mass of smoke appeared like phantom fangs that were ready to harm anyone who dared to inhale. The lower parts of the mass of bellowing smoke crisscrossed the sky. It was darker, thicker, and more somber. Higher up, the smoke seemed lighter, moved faster, and looked less menacing. The thickest of the smoke remained just above the ground. There, it seemed to cast a spell of desolation. The desolation was made all the more menacing by the tall buildings that intersected the smoke-filled sky.

Ko-Ofie craved for fresh air. But he knew from experience that if he opened the window, the polluted air would invade his lungs and force him to cough.

"Afua, I'm tired; I'm going to sleep."

"Well, what else can you do now? Yes, go and sleep. I am watching TV."

Later on, Afua went to the bedroom and found Ko-Ofie fast asleep. She knelt beside the bed and looked at his brooding face for a long time. This was the man every girl in his hometown had hoped to marry. This was the man who had just returned from these parts. How lucky she was for winning the communal competition that enabled him to marry her.

"But that was then and this is now. The youthful part of my life is gone. It's a dream that never materialized," whispered Afua, as she explored Ko-Ofie's forlorn face.

Ko-Ofie turned on his side and said, "I wasn't dreaming. Far from it! I was just dozing off. Can't you leave me alone for a few seconds? I just want to sleep, that's what I said."

Who cares about that? That's all you do when you come back from your potato-cutting job. I was just thinking about how I followed you to these parts to lose the best part of my life worth living."

Ko-Ofie cleared his throat, and replied, "How do you know if you've lost the best part of your life when you've never lived it at all?"

"Ko-Ofie dream on. I say dream on! After all, life here is a dream. The best life, you mean in these parts? Life! Whoever, thinks about the best life in these parts?"

Afua paused as if she was waiting for a reply from Ko-Ofie and when she realized that none was forthcoming she angrily continued, "Oh! Then, you did very well. You told the whole community about the wealth in these parts! Your own wealth! Their wealth! And the happiness that one could find in these parts. Now tell me, what did you leave out?"

"I explained everything! I told it as it was. Things have changed." That's too simple an answer. What's it that has changed so much to make us so miserable? Why do we keep coming to these parts? What changed? Tell me." "I've nothing to tell you."

"There you go again! You've not had anything to say since you came here. What you have been able to tell everyone is what your Western education has taught you. Yes, what they taught you to tell the underclass and the benighted Africans."

"But Afua, this defies simple answers."

"It's not an issue of simple answers or bigger questions. It's about your inability to come up with simple questions about our predicament, let alone answers."

"What do you mean by that? I just want to sleep."

But Afua ignored him and began to explain, "It's not only Africa's youths that want to come to these parts. This time around, everyone, including the aged! The aged encourage the youth to travel to these parts. For, the aged are also beneficiaries of the velvet. It gives them false longevity. It gives them false comfort. It's also the idea that their families have also made the journey to these parts."

"Well, a very comfortable situation then," Ko-Ofie intoned. "No! It brings acute suffering to the aged," Afua retorted. Ko-Ofie replied, "How do you know? And so what?"

"Yes, the youth are not there to see the aged die, or to sweeten their dried throats with eternal water for the journey to the other world. And none is there to close their mouths so that enough breath will be stored for the journey. And there is none to hear the secrets and the death wishes of the aged. Therefore, wisdom vanishes with the death of the aged," Afua paused and sat down on the bed.

Ko-Ofie moved slightly to his side of the bed, and mumbled, "You know, thinking about all these is very uncomfortable. It brings us pangs of pain. That's what it brings."

"I agree with you. But why do we keep coming!"

Afua's mind wandered away from Ko-Ofie's bleached face. She thought about the

50

source of their unhappiness and asked, "Ko-Ofie, why do people back home celebrate us? It is a paradox right? Is it because we are in these parts suffering?"

Ko-Ofie didn't volunteer any answer.

Afua retorted "Oh! You're dozing off, already dead!"

****

The strain on Ko-Ofie's face as sleep entombed him was horrifying. It came from a deep undefined within. Very deep and well-within. It was deep, deep down, depicted by his sonorous breathing. Even sleep, the majesty of all rest, was notable to dull and alleviate his deep-seated pain.

****

Afua raised Ko-Ofie's head and placed it in her lap. She startedcaressing his face, but stopped. His face was rough and had scars from ages of bleaching. She brushed her palm across her own face and felt the roughness from bleaching.

****

Afua got up from the bed and made her way to the bathroom. She opened the side drawer and took an AMBI cream, MADE IN U.S.A., and brought it out from its white container. She openedthe seal, smeared her fingers with the cream, and applied it to her face. It was a practiced ritual. And it was a ritual that gave birth to an assumed white beauty.

Moving closer to the mirror, Afua began to massage her face with the AMBI cream. Simultaneously, she caressed the idyllic picture of a white woman on the AMBI container. She placed the AMBI into its white container. Finally, she placed the AMBI at its eternal resting place in a white side drawer with its fluffy inside.

Afua cleaned her lips, nose, and chin with the velvet. She felt the pain from bleaching and wondered why she labored at it for so long. There was blood. She cleaned the blood and stood before the mirror for a long time. It was the mirror of her new birth. Yet it was a reflection of the old and dying self. It was a painful rebirth. The umbilical cord was not cut, but bleached. It was the birth of a new identity that came with wrinkles, aging, and pain.

Peering at her image in the mirror of her white rebirth, Afua slowly paced back and forth in the bathroom as if she was lost and needed to find her way out.

Chapter Three

The wind outside blew over Afua's face and sharpened the pain from bleaching. She touched her forehead with her middle finger. The AMBI cream was there.

Afua sat on a bench at the center of the park.

Nearby, a thirty-something white woman sat oblivious to the world. She looked regal, but wore a saggy and wrinkled face.

Examining her own skin, Afua clinically looked at the thirty-something white woman's wrinkled skin.

The thirty-something white woman returned Afua's apparent gaze, touched her own skin, and began to move away from the center to a peripheral area of the park. She continued to keep a distance between herself and Afua. As she moved, she touched different parts of her saggy and wrinkled body.

Afua wondered why the thirty-something white woman touched her own skin at the very areas that Afua had bleached.

Looking for a spot to sit down, Afua found a bench near a tree. She sat down, opened her hand bag, and brought out an old photo album.

She looked up and the thirty-something white woman was merging with the smog that was gradually eclipsing her wrinkles.

For a moment, the smog became lighter and Afua could see the thirty-something white woman point at her own face.

Simultaneously, Afua touched the area between her forehead and nose and found blood. Foraging into her handbag, Afua brought out an AMBI user's guide and read the instructions. After this, she folded the Ambi users' guide with religious zeal. She closed her eyes as if she was praying and began to ritually clean blood between the ridge of her nose and lower forehead with a blood-stained velvet.

When Afua opened her eyes, the thirty-something white woman was completely enveloped by the smog.

****

Afua opened photo album. It contained photos of her most recent visit to Ghana.

The first photo showed the entrance to a church building. It was elegantly draped with velvets. Afua recognized the velvets. They belonged to her. She had donated them to the church.

The onlookers in the photo were wearing broad smiles: the velvet apparently had a universal appeal in Ghana.

The most prominent figure in the photo was the officiating pastor. His imposing figure was like someone paying homage to the gods and goddesses of the velvets. Afua was his goddess, the giver of abundant grace from these parts, symbolized by her donation of velvets to the church.

****

The history of the velvet is a paradox and an unchanging one. It is epistemologically told in the present tense. The onlookers in the photo know very little about how the velvet is acquired. Yet they worship it. They are the worshippers. They are the very people who have the capacity to appreciate the intrinsic value of the velvet. They have imbibed the velvet seekers' dream without understanding its implications. Of course, they know that anyone who travels to these parts is bound to return home with the cargo and its best symbolism is the velvet.

The calculation is that velvet seekers who do not often return to Africa have not done their homework well. Simply put, they have failed to acquire velvets in these parts. And such unsuccessful velvet seekers have failed themselves and the homegets who are the recipients of the velvets in Africa. But there is a ring of comfort to it. Even those who fail to bring the velvet home, but brave the odds to make the return journey to Africa are entertained, though not worshipped. In sum, the homegets have unstated influence on the velvet seekers. The homegets are not passive. And they spare none who returns home without a velvet.

The worshippers appreciate the cargoes acquired by the velvet seekers, and as a result the worshippers see the velvet seekers as the heroes and heroines of modern Africa. In the garbled language of the worshippers, the velvet seekers have arrived. The achievements of the velvet seekers can be infectious. Also, its virus infects African youths who then develop the urge to take to ritualized flights from their places of birth to these parts by any means possible.

****

African passports are the global license for the new slave trade. It is also called brain drain. The passport and visas to travel to these parts have become symbolisms of putative belonging. Traveling to these parts are also associated with the universal African dream. And the dream is defined by the elusive American Dream transposed onto Africa via satellites that HOLLYwudize unsuspecting Africans. In the garbled language of Western hegemony, it is now known as Globalization. It is the unidirectional migration of non-African values, policies, goals, practices, ideologies, goods, etc. into Africa. It is another form of Western imperialism euphemistically called Globalization. And some call it popular culture.

Oh! The lure of the dream to live in these parts has many antecedents. It includes coca cola! Pepsi! Chocolate bars! Ice cream!

Ah! These days the African dream includes Kentucky Fried Chicken (KFC), Burger King. Not that these are not available on African markets. They are. These are the foods and drinks of the middle class. Yes, the educated pen-armed robbers of postcolonial Africa. Pen-armed robbers who steal from the state to enrich themselves. Their cargo cult is expensive cars. Have five of them and you are a successful person. Their food is pizza, KFC, Chinese perfumed rice, burger king, and all. They attend classes to learn how to use Japanese chop sticks.

And the effects are there for all to see: fat couples and their bloated children struggling to walk through the doors of KFC! Fattened old men, both white and black, struggling to take their young teenage girlfriends to KFC, Burger King, and all. For that is where young African females in the company of old white men yearn to eat. And yes, young males in the company of old white tourists are not left out. Those food joints are their hangouts. To be seen there inhaling the aroma of KFC and all are a life-saving venture for the lost youths of Africa.

But there is a riddle to all these. These foods and drinks have colonized African markets. But the African middle class, the pen-armed robbers, still want to travel to these parts to taste the real homemade KFC, Burger King, and all in these parts. Indeed a seam of the postcolonial dream of the pen-armed robbers, also called "stealers." Yes, pen-armed robbers and stealers, whose one signature can rob a whole country of its wealth. And the pen-armed robbers are worshipped, yes, regaled, and adored for their stolen wealth.

Another alluring agency is nude white women plastered on sweating beer bottles, known as commercials or ads. And Western beaches turned into citadels of sexual parade. And Africans imitate all these to show that they have arrived in the precincts of Western civilization.

The above are not the essential elements. They only facilitate the African dream of traveling to these parts. They serve as an initiation for the real dream. The actual dream includes the acquisition of cars, TVs, VCRs, fridges, toasters, washing machines, sound systems, plush furniture, IPods, IPads, IPhones, etc. Sadly, none of these is manufactured in Africa. These are the superstructures of the cargo-cult mentality of velvet seekers and their worshippers alike.

Fruition of the dream, yes the fruition of the dream, is the acquisition of Euro-American accents. The fruition comes with family celebrations, especially when the Euro-American accents of children of velvet seekers attain a state of flawlessness. Even those in Africa who don't have that drawls, twangs, and inflections pride themselves with "gonna" and "wanna" in every sentence.

****

But all these frantic dreams have their limitations! It is a velvet seeker's ability to spread and multiply the dollar, the pound sterling, the Yen, and the Euro that says it all. It is a ritual that determines whether a velvet seeker would be worshiped or not.

In order to get the utmost regal worship, a velvet seeker has to put relatives, towns-folks, and country-folks on the new slave ships. This is a major transition in life: from a worshipper to a velvet seeker. And it is also the culmination of the universal African dream.

The worshippers are not wholly to be blamed. The blame is at the doors of the velvet seekers. Those who have shrines and monuments erected in their honor; they are the ones who should carry the blame. They are the ones who have woefully failed to tell the truth about these parts: the suffering, the alienation, the marginalization, above all the otherness and othering. The velvet seekers have substituted the killing of the soul in these parts for dreams they no longer believe in. They are cultural orphans, marginalized in their mortgaged homes, secluded offices, and hostile workplaces.

****

But these are not all the paradoxes of inferiority. There are billboards in Africa that announce that freedom and wealth exist in these parts. The billboards are decorated with amiable, elderly whites with sweets lurking between their decaying teeth. And there are billboards decorated with white women embossed on sweating beer bottles. Ah! Western influence can be found in white-complexioned mannequins that are symbols of Western fashions in the mode of cheap Chinese-made dresses in African shops. And Africans prefer these cheap foreign clothes that reveal unholy body parts to sacrosanct and aesthetically made African local wear.

Yes, the African blind love for anything foreign can be found in African barbershops where Western celebrities showcase indigenous African hairstyles that were once tagged barbaric by whites. Today white soccer stars wear the once considered barbaric haircuts with pride and magisterial arrogance.

And local hair saloons pregnant with pictures of foreign femalewearing long wavy hair are all over the place. Lacking the natural long wavy hair of White celebrities, African females of all ages shop in such saloons for wavy goat hairs from India and wavy horse hairs from Brazil. The task of shopping for varietiesof wavy hairs have been made easier by Chinese-made wavy hairs, better still white hair. Ironically, Chinese women wear their own hair, not the wavy hair they export to Africa! Africanwomen no longer like their natural hair! The bigger and longer the imported wavy hair the better, paradoxically a signifier of the colonized damaged psyche of inferiority.

****

There is also the African educational system that celebrates these parts in curricula and syllabi. Hence, students learn moreabout these parts than Africa. They learn about Buckingham Palace, River Thames, Appalachian Mountains, Eiffel Tower, Great Lakes, Corn Belt, Niagara Falls, George Washington, Abraham Lincoln, Churchill, and the Victorians, indeed name them! Cadillac, Ford, Chrysler and all! What is called African History is the study of European activities in Africa.

****

The only credible African history is oral history of Africa told by Africans themselves. No matter its fluidity, mutability, and selectivity of detail, African orality is the watershed of authentic African history. Most Western scholars of African history on the pedestal of fame don't speak and neither do they understand the nuances of African languages. As a result, most Western historians of African history, especially the contemporary generation, don't use oral history harvested from the very people they study and write about. They rely on the violence of Western texts cobbled by biased and even racist colonial officials, Christian missionaries, and adventurer-travelers as their key sources of African history.

And local African newspapers, radios, and TV programs propagate these parts in several ways. They champion foreign music, foreign films or movies, Yankee slangs, mother's day, father's day, sister's day, brother's day, lover's day, and several other days of emptiness constructed in these parts to promote capitalism. But the elites of African newspapers, radios, and TV programs have forgotten about Ghanaian days! Of course African-oriented days do not count. Very soon, African newspapers, radios, and TV programs will highlight Chinese dog days and Japanese chop sticks days. And African journalists, like African academics, are willing to quote any perspectives on Africa from Western sources with no questions asked.

Remember the nursing rhyme in African schools! The best comes from the West!

****

We keep borrowing from others, indeed, stealing from others, while we forget and denigrate our own values and cultures. And we do so without asking critical questions!

****

Afua removed another picture from the album. She raised it above her head as if for a better examination and contemplation, but eventually placed the photo on the bench. She took another picture from the album. This one was taken during the Annual District Church Harvest. Afua was the chairperson for the occasion. The picture portrayed palm fronds. Studded with flowers, the palm fronds formed an arc around her.

****

Afua had wondered about the use of natural flowers in creating the arc. It was during the peak of the dry season, and naturally- grown flowers were difficult to come by. But there was an assurance in the flamboyant display. The pastor had announced, "These flowers are solely groomed for Afua. They will always be there for her, people like her. We're happy to say that Afua is the ninth person to grant us this veritable honor of donating velvets to our community. It's our wish that many more will return home with the velvet and donate it to the church."

The congregation happily responded, "Thank you very much.

You're our true daughter"

Egged on, the Pastor continued in an assuring tone, "We planted and irrigated the flowers with holy water. The money came from the congregation. After all, one good turn deserves another. And besides, it's for our spiritual growth, in fact, for all of us."

****

Afua had always wondered about the Pastor's metaphor. And Ko-Ofie, who had also questioned the meaning of the pastor's speech, had stated that local churches and religious groups have become a part of the cargo cult mentality.

Afua had asked, "They become what?"

"Oh you know what I'm talking about. These are pastors and priests who ride in Mercedes and Lexus, and whose ill-acquired riches have sown the seeds of immorality."

"I see! It's true that church officials use the name of God to preyupon poor workers, the unemployed, and subsistence farmers."

"How do they that?"

Afua brushed some locks of hair from her forehead and said, "Oh they are exploited at two levels. Let me make it simple for you. Level one concerns political and religious exploitation. These Pastors, Prophets, Overseers, and Priests study at seminariesin

Africa where they are taught that African religions and worldviews are atavistic and immemorial. Such leaders of the Church then receive terminal degrees from backyard Western Bible and theological institutions where the demonization of African religions and worldview are at their summits. The essence of their whole education is about how to reject African religions. That means Africans are called upon to reject the African way of life."

"Anyway, so what's the second level?"

"The second level concerns alienation from the African environment and the constant yearning for the material things that these parts offer. Africans now hate themselves because they've bought into the ways that whites demonize them as the inferior other."

Kofi smiled wryly and intoned "That's well-said, my priestess!"

****

Pondering over her musings with Ko-Ofie, Afua dangled thephoto in her hand as if she was looking for further explanations.

****

Afua looked into the skies as though she could find someanswers to her overcrowding thoughts. She opened the next page of the album and found a newspaper clip. It was a review of a book that demonized Kwame Nkrumah.

****

She closed the album with the hope that she could stop feeding on the squalor of her mind's eye.

The media and academics' lopsided viewpoints from theseparts are recycled and assimilated by African scholars and the African media. Prostituted African scholars and media people present hobbling and jaundiced African social and political epistemologies, infesting the youth of Africa with theirEurocentric Africanisms.

African scholars and the African media have let down the masses of Africa. For a long time, the masses of Africa havenot been certain about African history. Was the African voice in African history prompted by the ambitions of Africans, or the underhand schemes of the West? There is always a school, an idea, and an interpretation that one can trust and reframe as one's own. But indentured African scholars pander to Westernscholars, schools, and media, yet see themselves as the sages of modern Africa. These academic vassals see themselves as Africa's best and brightest in the service of the Western voice.

Popularized by the indentured African scholars and white plantation-owner scholars, the Africa is but anything that loomslarge in the distorted imaginings of the muse of history. The plantation-owner scholars are still the best. An irony. No Africanstirs the pot of American history, British history, Canadian history, Chinese history and others. These are exclusive preserve of scholars who hail from those countries. But African history is a free range for even white tourist scholars, who havenot cut their teeth, to colonize the terrain as specialist. It's an irony. Simply, the best comes from the West. Hmmm! The firstthing that African toddlers learn in their cradles and nurseries of education.

The African elites have one major enthusiasm. It is to maintain their bestowed popularity gained from these parts. Therefore, they see Africa from the distorted lens of those Africanists from these parts. Africanists from these parts give the African scholarsthe paradigmatic props to hoist their warped interpretations of Africa. You see them at conferences organized by the Africanists of these parts to promote their own agenda: their professional credentials, win grants, serve on editorial boards, and set agenda for African studies.

The study of Africa will continue to be a sham. Although it's a huge business now, more importantly, it has become a cottage industry. It is a huge business controlled by the scholars and academia of these parts. These scholars from these parts remove themselves into Africa for a few months and return home with all the answers. The irony is that they never go back to see changes overtime. They hold onto their stale historical ideologies. They become the specialists in diverse Africa/na fields. Then there are those who have never been to Africa, buthave all the antidotes, all the answers! And above all, there are those who sit in the comfort of air-conditioned offices in these parts and buy cheap untrained African labor with dollars to do their field and archival researches in Africa for them. The result is also African history.

Indeed, these are the specialists in African/a studies! They offer no meaningful scholarship on Africa. Nor do they provide new movements away from the merry Africa, from the primitive Africa, and from immemorial Africa. They are the editors of publishing houses, journals, and magazines on Africa. And they are consultants for hire by the Big Bank of the World. And they belong to the Big Bank of the World that sees to the exploitation of Africa's human and natural resources.

****

Afua was aware that Ko-Ofie knew about all these too. For, he had said that he was part of the problem. She remembered the last Christmas get-together and the perspectives on Africa that emerged. In the end no one said much. Everybody was, it seemed to her, afraid to say "I am going home forever, and hence death to the velvet, indeed, death to the Western cargo, their so-called civilization!"

Some velvet seekers don't want anyone to broach the subject of Africa and the question of returning home. Some Africans in these parts vomit whenever the subject of returning home is broached.

"You know you've eaten what doesn't belong to you," Afua had once reprimanded her Christmas guest.

The guest laughed and phlegm flowed freely from his nostrils.

Afua screamed and said, "Everyone, come and see, he's draining off all the foreign elements in his body. It's surprising how the mere mention of returning home makes you feel whole again by vomiting the dregs of deadly nightmares experienced in these parts."

"Yes," replied the guest, "It makes me feel good about myself. But you know it is also makes me feel like a failure, indeed, very empty."

"Eh! So all along you thought you were a winner? You thought you were successful! You are the worst of the failures, in fact, the most despicable. You even vomited the little you've acquired here too. We should remember that we are failures, not heroes or heroines to the dead, living, and unborn Africans," Afua had paused for effect.

Raising her voice that eclipsed the vomiting sounds in the bathroom, Afua had continued, "I think that all of us need to vomit like he has, but not at the thought of going home. We need to vomit long before coming here. The thought of it should make us vomit. And this should even occur before we travel to these parts. In other words, we should stay and develop our local resources, not hanker after a radiant dream that melts with the touch of reality."

****

But there are twists to such things. The tangle lies with the velvetseekers. The velvet seekers experience pain and anguish in the mega cities of these parts. But the velvet seekers don't tell the worshippers and homegets at home the truth about their lived-experiences in these parts. Velvet seekers tell flavored lies about love, accommodation, inclusion, and assimilation. All the best, if a velvet seeker tells his or her story in some auctioned accents of these parts. Yes, BBC accent, or Yankee slang is the best. These days, even Dubai accents have gained grounds. Ah! Not to forget Chinese, South Korean, and Indian Englishes. These are a boardroom assets that African elites acquire. Such fleetingstories of friendliness, inclusion, and wealth told in borrowed accents are dramatized to carry some meanings. And so such stories come with laughter and tears of joy, though emanate from dizzying spells of pain within, deep, deep within.

****

Afua looked at the picture once more. She tried to recapture the vivid essences of the Pastor's sermon. The Pastor had stressed that there was no need to read from the Bible. He claimed that Afua was with them in spirit and that her fair complexion was a text on its own that can benefit the day's sermon.

The Pastor focused on her and told the congregation that it was essential for them to adore her while he preached.

After paying tribute to the previous velvet

donors, the Pastor proclaimed, "God has helped Afua in her travels, we thank Him. We thank Him for nourishing Afua for all of us," amidst a sonorous punctuation of "Amen, Amen" from the congregation.

"Today our sister, Afua, is in our midst, look at her curves, look at her fair complexion, her wavy hair, and her Shakespearean speech patterns, Amen. Why? She prayed hard. That's why God has helped her. How many of us here are willing, and I mean willing and truly willing to sacrifice, indeed travel to these parts to bring home those beautiful velvet draperies for the Church? Afua has not only brought them, praise the Lord! She has donated all to our church!

After the sermon, the congregation lined up to greet Afua. When it was over, Afua sat stolidly in a chair with her head in her lap.

A Presbyter cleared his throat and said, "Afua, are you okay?"

Afua lifted up her head and confronted the gaze of the Presbyter. She bent down her head to avoid his gaze. Her smoldering eyes met the reflection of her bleached face on the glass-top table. She raised her head to escape her own apparition. But her eyes, once again, met the gaze of the Presbyter.

Winking at Afua, the Presbyter wrestled with her eyes, as his penetrating gaze journeyed onto her mid-section.

Afua avoided the Presbyter's combative eyes and focused more attention on the Pastor who was folding one of the velvets.

The bright lights in the ante-room brightened the contours of the crumpled velvet.

The Pastor handed one part of the velvet to Afua, called the Presbyter, and said, "We need your help to fold the velvet. It's heavy and slippery-like."

As they tried to fold up the velvet, it kept slipping out of their iron-clad gripping fingers. Afua clung hard to the velvet in order to hold on to it. Afua outstretched her legs to get a stronger footing to hold onto her end-piece of the velvet. To her surprise, as she looked up, she found the Presbyter's gaze fixed at her mid-section. And both of their eyes met the Pastor's who was licking his pursed lips.

The Presbyter's searing gaze at her mid-section warmed Afua's memories. It brought delight to the enclave of her thighs.

And the Presbyter's eyes continued to burrow into Afua's mid-section. Afua had felt the approach of an unsolicited pleasure. It felt like she was having a warm bath after being in the cold for a long time. Suddenly, she dropped her end of the velvet and sat in a chair.

Afua's surging joy intensified.

Seizing the arms of the chair, Afua blurted out, "Hold the velvet.

Pick up the velvet! Oh hold it! Lift up the velvet!"

A searing jolt of pleasure quaked Afua's body. As she fell off the chair, she heard the Pastor's harrowing voice echoing, "Get up, daughter! Get up dutiful daughter of the velvet, Ah! Get up! Amen!"

When Afua came to, the Presbyter who

was holding one endof the velvet said, "I covered you with the velvet with thehope of satisfying you. You know that the velvet is a powerful demonstration of our faith in cargo-cult."

Afua's eyes flooded with tears. She thought the Pastor and the Presbyter were collaborators in all her sufferings in these parts.

Caught in a ritualized frenzy, the Pastor and the Presbyter danced about. They pranced about with the velvet like children chasing butterflies in a children's playground. They placed thevelvet on the floor and began to clap their hands. As they did so, the Presbyter asked Afua to join them.

Afua shook her head and began to move away. But she trippedon the velvet and fell down. She sat up and pleaded with themto let her go home. Then the Pastor brought out a bottle of holywater from his side-pocket and sprinkled it on the spot where Afua had tripped.

The holy water on the velvet gave way to a terrible nauseating smell. And both the Pastor and the Presbyter grabbed the velvet and began to whirl it around with enthusiasm to clear the putridsmell. In the process, the arresting scent took over the whole church room.

Afua summoned courage: she finally decided to tell them aboutthe story of the velvet. But, abruptly the Presbyter stopped whirling the velvet and covered his nostrils with it. After inhaling for some time, he inserted two ends of the velvet into his nostrils. Leaning against the pulpit, he clapped his hands, and began to hum a hymn.

A scuffle ensued between the Pastor and the Presbyter for the velvet. Eventually, the velvet straddled the neck of the Presbyter and the Pastor succeeded in grasping one end of the twirled velvet away from the Presbyter and snaked it around his own neck.

Afua, who was still sitting on the floor pleaded with them to stop.

Finally, the Presbyter let out a scream as the Pastor pulled the velvet.

The Pastor let go the velvet and took Afua's hand, saying that "We are united in a trinity forever."

The Pastor looked into Afua's eyes for affirmation and continued, "I won't let anyone desecrate the velvet. It's something holy in our hands. It's all that the masses of Ghana need. And you've brought it. You brought it to us. Afua you're the moral pillar and repository of Euro-Christian mores. The masses of Ghana and Africa will forever thank you. We're forever grateful to you."

Afua had looked unconcernedly at the Pastor. The Pastor pulled up Afua from the floor.

Afua closed her eyes, took short steps, and allowed the Pastor to pull her along.

The Pastor looked at her and spoke slowly, "Err, it's all right. Over there where you live and work, I guess there are no problems. Everything is on a silver platter. It's like when you put the velvet on the church's platter."

Afua hated the priest for his parabolic

speech, but hated herself the more for not telling them about the story of the velvet: the truth for once! But it was not her fault. No! Not at all.

****

The velvet seekers have chosen to whittle away life in these parts. It entails laboring in all forms. It entails African PhD holders cutting potatoes. History PhD holders tenured as laboratory assistants in archeology labs. Civil engineers who measure the sizes of wedding cakes. Meteorologists washing cars in the aftermath of thunderstorms. Accountants turned toll collectors on highways. Medical doctors serving as mortuary assistants. Social workers dutifully cleaning and massaging the private parts of old, forgotten so-named senior citizens. Geographers measuring distances covered by taxis driven by fellow Africans. These and others are the velvet seekers who have shrines built in their honor in Africa! They are Africa's best brains. But above all, they are velvet seekers who embody the stark future of Africa because of collective inferiorization, the product of slavery, colonialism, neocolonialism, and globalization.

Afua smiled wryly, and whispered "Ko-Ofie, PhD Engineering (Toronto), and still potato-cutting!"

****

But people like Afua without higher

academic degrees also suffer daily. They are also trapped in a pit of quicksand. The problem is not physical. It is mental. That is the most painful part. One can always pretend that everything is okay. One can pretend that nothing has happened. For, there is nothing physical about it to show. But within that mental entity, thereis always a simmering death. And it is the dying of the soul. It entails a social death. It leads to the rejection of existence itself.It is a premature death. And it comes before the actual death. It comes in the midst of perceived abundance of the cargoes in these parts. It is a cult without a god or a goddess. Therefore the materiality that lures the velvet seekers to these parts is a social death in itself. And it is prefaced by loneliness of the soul.

It comes with the intense yearning of the heart, poverty of the mind, and decay of the body before the actual death.

****

Tears besieged Afua's eyes as she thought about the past and what the future held for her. She realized that she was not alone,and she muttered, "Who will be in the photo next!"

****

Afua placed the photo on the ones she had examined. She opened another page of the album. This time the velvet had found a home in the official residence of the Pastor. There weredifferent velvets in the photo. The photo had blood-like spots indicating the names some velvet seekers who had donated velvets to the church.

****

Afua looked up and the saw the passing clouds. It was journeyingwith some itinerant smog. Darkness was approaching. She putthe photos in the album and started for home.

Along the way, she heard some disturbing footsteps in the distance. The foot-steps belonged to the thirty-something white woman.

The thirty-something white woman stopped, touched some withering flowers, and smiled at Afua.

Afua stopped in her tracks, paused for a while, and began to walk away.

The thirty-something white woman touched the sagging wrinkles in the region of her neck, called up to Afua, and said, "I've tanned enough, right!"

I'm sorry, I didn't hear you well," Afua replied.

The thirty-something white woman responded, "There are many questions we ask without getting answers! You know! You see these flowers," the thirty-something white womanpointed at the flowers and continued, "I want to know when they will shrivel!"

"Oh so you came here to ask such vague questions!"

"We ask questions all the time. All of us do."

"Certainly, I don't dispute that. But questions should be meaningful."

"Well, I brought my whiteness to the sun, and I asked the sun ifI had tanned enough! These are meaningful questions. But the sun never responded!"

"Is that so? Is that all? You came here to get a tan?"

"Yes, I will see you next summer. You appear to like whiteness.Leave your acquired, imaginary whiteness and come and tan with me next summer. It would do you good. Bye, my dear," said the thirty-something white woman.

Chapter Four

Afua looked around. Darkness had begun to rule space, eclipsing the smog.

She walked briskly.

The corridor was very dark, as it had always been.She opened the door.

She thought about the various contours of her marriage with Ko-Ofie.

Ko-Ofie coughed in the bedroom.

Afua walked into the bedroom and found Ko-Ofie in bed. His supine posture evoked something in her: they had not made love in a long time.

Ko-Ofie coughed again, and Afua remarked, "Have you taken your medicine?"

"Yes, I did."

"When was the last time you took it?" Afua asked emphatically. But Ko-Ofie didn't provide any answer!

"You won't answer me! I know. What about these? Afuaqueried, as she pointed to some magazines on the bed.

"Please, leave me alone. I just want to sleep."

"Oh, now you want to sleep with those in the magazines! I remember all those pornographic movies that you broughtto Ghana. Thousands are regularly sent to Africa. They are acquired by the rich, famous, and educated people like you. Worse, they are now free on cellphone, oh, bestiality and all."

"Oh, Afua not again, let me sleep. Please! No lectures. Oh! Notright now."

"Don't lie to me. It's not that you want to

sleep; it's the reference to the educated elites that you don't want to hear."

"Pausing for effect, Afua continued," The politicians have their share of pornography. In fact, they have the largest collections. Pornography adorn their offices, cars, and rented hotel rooms. And it's the state that pays for such carnal corruption."

"Afua, please, let us discuss this later," Ko-Ofie pleaded.

"Don't fool me. When was the last time we had any discussion? Let me tell the world what's on my chest. If you want to sleep, the rest of the world is awake. And I'm now the rest of the world. Oh! Ko-Ofie, I'm well awake now."

"Okay, go ahead and tell the world, but not here."

"Yes, I know. Certainly, not here, of course! This home is dead anyway. You are dead anyway. Therefore, who cares about you? I will continue and you better listen to me, dead or alive."

"Please go ahead and talk if that is what makes you happy."

"Yes, I want us to be happy, my husband. I want to rescue you from your present state."

Afua moved closer to Ko-Ofie, placed her legs on his thighs, and began to caress his thighs. But Ko-Ofie didn't respond.

Afua asked, "Ko-Ofie, do you remember that joke?"

"Now, you have moved from preaching to jokes! What joke are you talking about?"

"Oh, the joke about husbands who work at four jobs and return home so tired that they can hardly move their waists!"

"And is that funny?"

"It's a joke. I know it. But it has happened to you. For you it's not a joke. It's the reality of your life. You sleep very well at table as well as in bed. It's the same in the bedroom as it's at the table. Anytime I turn to face you in bed, you increase your snoring. Ha ha, it's your snoring that tells me no, no, yet all I wish to know!"

Afua smiled to herself and began to undress. She slid into bed beside Ko-Ofie, but he groaned and moved closer to the wall. Afua propped herself on her left hand and looked at Ko-Ofie's face. She brushed aside a wet tuft of permed hair from his forehead. Ko-Ofie pushed Afua's hand away and edged closer to the wall.

Moving closer to Ko-Ofie, Afua clasped her fingers around her firm breasts. Her nipples were surrounded by well-spaced aureoles. She touched the aureoles on her left breast and her nipple stood at their full length.

Then she took Ko-Ofie's hands and clasped them on her right breast. Ko-Ofie slightly adjusted his shoulders, pulled his hand away, and murmured something that made no sense to Afua.

"I've been starved for a long time. Is this how it ended? That's too soon. So you don't have anything to offer any more. Not even caressing me?"

Ko-Ofie sat up on the bed and put his left hand around Afua. Caressing Afua's nape with his right fingers, he intoned, "Afua, I still love you. I wish to God that you understand my situation."

"I don't understand? What? Am I a stranger to be told this! I dounderstand! It's you and your likes who don't understand! You can't put the blame at the doors of everyone. It's just here with us. It's at our door. Yes, just this door," Afua protested, as she pointed to the door to their room.

"Yes, I know all about what you are saying. I don't just feel well. Just go and do something interesting."

"Oh, I'm a bitch right! And I'm in heat! Okay, I'm going out. Any man I find today will take over our bed. I suppose this home will be his too!"

Afua looked brazenly at Ko-Ofie and emphatically intoned, "I must tell you that I haven't enjoyed life with you. The first nightI slept with you, it was stale sex and it has remained so to date.I kept thinking about the happiness you promised me."

"I never promised you anything. I promised you a good marriage."

"That is a promise. You promised me life and wealth, but not marriage. You don't know what marriage is about. It's not whenyou get a few dollars from the pain and humiliation in these parts, and you go home to deceive every woman you meet."

"So why did you marry me? I didn't promise you wealth, but marriage."

"Yes, if you promised me marriage, where is it anyway? And where is the wealth? I haven't found it anywhere, not here in these parts! And certainly not with you either! This is not an area of happiness. I would rather die than remain here forever. I still think about the riches you promised my parents."

"I did not promise your parents riches."

"Oh, you did. Not only that! You even promised every woman in the town. I never could bring myself to believe that. You said that you had all things under the snow. How funny, under the snow eh!"

"Afua, oh, that was the art of courtship and nothing more!" "Ko-Ofie, that was wrong then and a tragedy now." "What? Did you say a tragedy?"

"Your life, mine, and all others have been rendered tragic. Look at your living room, bedroom, and bank account. You were not the engineer you claimed you were. Hello! Not even a technical assistant. With all your education you are a potato- cutter, a profession without a name. Shame on you! With all your education, I have had to coin a name for your profession.

Afua paused, hoping that Ko-Ofie, who had cleared his throat, would say something, but, Ko-Ofie only looked on gloomily, as if what Afua was saying had nothing to do with him.

Afua looked at him pensively, and continued, "Besides, I'm getting bored with all that you've to say. Why can't you say something more concrete?"

Afua paused again for effect, as if she was addressing a room full of people, who were disillusioned with these parts, and continued, "I tell you, you're the subject of laughter and ridicule in our community."

Ko-Ofie retorted, "What about laughter and whose community?"

"I know your shoulders are weak because of hours on end of potato-cutting. You stand on your toes all day and all night, some engineer you have become."

"Oh, save it. At least, I've my degrees."

"Not here. That is why I said that death would be better for us. Is this the relevance of all the education you've had, I mean you and the so-called intellectuals."

"Will you shut up?"

"Will I shut up? Is that all you can say? Is your mouth also impotent? I won't shut up anytime soon. Not for anything! Never ever say that to me again. For, you don't own me and I don't owe you a thing. I want to say to you that I'm sick, and we're dying, dead and dead."

****

Ko-Ofie left the bedroom and stood by the window in the livingroom, the one that offered a better view of the outside. The room was dull. Everything was at a standstill. It seemed not even the air moved. Far away, he watched as car lights penetrated the smog.

Pondering over Afua's words, Ko-Ofie smiled. He came to the conclusion that Afua's complaints were nothing new. But, tonight she had made her point. She had linked her complaints with his lack of interest in life. Surprisingly, he was not hurt. He had seen it coming long ago. What he hadn't expected was the authority, venom, and

84

abandon with which she had said it.

Ko-Ofie put his arms on the window pane, and the cold glass intensified his pain. There was pain all over his body, especially in his waist. A little sleep would have alleviated the pain. He went for an armchair, placed it by the window, and sat down. It felt somewhat better. The pain in his waist receded, but the feverish headache remained. It was sleep he needed, but not Afua's scolding words.

****

Afua's criticisms have become an archive. The intellectual! Really! And what has he done for Ghana and Mother Africa? What has he done for the cocoa peasants whose sweat and money nurtured him and others in school?

"Oh! Where is all the care and love for one's country? Would I be cutting potatoes in Ghana? Would I have lost my very essence of being?"

As though he was speaking to Afua, he continued, "I understand what you meant by ideology! Afua, potato-cutting in these parts is a part of the ideology of African survival.

Ko-Ofie continued to lament, "It's meant for all of us. Each day, we are told everything in and from Africa is bad and must be transformed. Our policies have to be changed and modelled on those of these parts. Ironically, such recommendations for change do not come from Africans. The proposed change always comes from specialists from these parts, propagating the influence of outsiders, but not Africans, in fact, those within,who need the said change."

****

Afua walked into the living room, stood there for some time, and said soothingly, "Ko-Ofie, will you stop talking to yourself. Your doctor said that it's not good for you."

"Thanks Afua! I will keep my sickening thoughts to myself. Thatway neither you nor the doctor will know about my sickness."

****

Corruption! Unsurpassed corruption! Moral corruption in Ghana! Who teaches it? It's a paradox. People from these parts write the textbooks on corruption in Africa. But, the teachers who use the textbooks are African politicians. These politicians are bred in "Westernized" African classrooms. Their school fees are paid from the sweats of cocoa peasants, who never see or use cocoa butter, the product of their sweat. The process of transmutation from pupils to students and henceto scholars is in itself glorifying. For such transformation to occur, school children are projected by their communities as their future representatives in governments. Students' quests for Westernization is the communal key to their reverential selection.

****

African politicians are very much revered if they happen to belong to one of the following: Whiggish Cambridge-trained historians; Half-baked Sandhurst-trained soldiers; Ideologized Moscow-trained Marxists; Oxford-recruited anthropologists; Don Quixotic Sorbonne-preened literati; and Harvard-bottled coca cola MBAs. These are the training grounds for the sages of modern Africa. But these days, locally-trained politicians are making the rounds!

****

But there are local ones too. The Lagoonites on top of the depleting food chain of education. This is where colonial eschatology of education is highly respected. Then there is a College by the sea where sand in mobility is used for teaching experiments. The Savannah Citadels of learning, the flying pads for guinea fowls in flight from education. Ah Polytechnic schools on university pedestals where Ghanaian history is shunned in favor of making local pottery called STEM. All these are breeding grounds for "stealers," not the keepers of the faith of nation-building.

****

Then there are the insane majesties: the Socialists in capitalist garb. They used to wear goatees and dabble in languages of justice and equality. Their collective ideology was in waiting for political opportunities of crumbs from African dictators, especially the military elite. Overnight in PAJEROS, BMWS, MERCEDES, LEXUS, and JAGUARS, the Socialists shed off socialism. These are political chameleons that came into their own in the Age of Corruption and Graft during the 1979 Devolution.

****

All these African political elites and scholars have misled the masses of Africa on a path of fixation on these parts. No wonder Africans cross the Sahara to be sold into slavery, or at best pick fruits and harvest vegetables in Italy and Portugal. Africans cross the Arabian Sea to work as house servants for Arabs who abuse them. Africans cross the Atlantic to clean-up senior citizens of these parts abandoned in Old People's Homes! These days, Africans are crossing the South China Sea to work on Chinese farms. Simply put, the African universal dream is about out of Africa.

****

Some scholars have also constructed pseudo-schools of Darwinism beginning with Afridocism and Afrikadocity and the like. Such schools pontificate that Africans told stories this way, Africans married this way, African burials were like this and that. In all, Africa is still a prototype buried in a sarcophagus. Nothing changes. Not even rebirth in the aftermath of decay!

****

Ko-Ofie paused to recollect his thoughts. He felt dizzy. He brushed the back of his right hand across his face and stood up. The dizziness was suffocating. But his suffusing thoughts werepoints of healing. He held the arms of the chair as a means of support and sat down.

****

Also the African elites tutor African children to hunt for the fruit of knowledge of these parts. This is what the new Africais all about. The knowledge of these parts comes in different packages: acquisition of accents, dependence on birthday cakes, and an ability to quote a Shakespeare. And oh, we have Mother's Day! Granny's Decade! Father's Week! Grand-Pa's Month! Great-Great Grand-Pa's Year! Yes, Valentine's Day: thatis when all Africans celebrate love. And we keep borrowing celebrations and events. As a result, the rest of the world knows nothing about African cultures. Primitive Africa is still an assetin the West. CNN Africa is all about exotic animals, pop culture,cottage industries, touristic art in African settings.

****

Seized by a strong cough, Ko-Ofie went to the kitchen and poured himself a glassful of orange juice. On the counter, food,prepared days before, gallantly announced, "Dare you eat me?"

****

There is no hunger in these parts. Returning velvet seekers explain this with relish to the willing waiters and worshippers in Africa. It's an irony. In these parts, the African mind and body have the capacity to shut off the motor of hunger. There are many sides to it, indeed, contending polarities: the yearning of the body and the yearning of the soul are programmed by the desolation of the mind. And sometimes salivating comes with a dried-parched tongue. These are some of the paradoxes and the ironies that are never explained to the teeming worshippers back home in Africa.

****

Ko-Ofie surveyed the kitchen. It was as somber as his thoughts. Then he whispered, "Do I make sense at all?" Ko-Ofie heard his own voice, but there was no response to it. He placed the glass of orange juice on the counter and left the kitchen.

****

Standing at the window, Ko-Ofie tried to recollect his thoughts. He also felt like calling Afua to his aid. At least, Afua's presence would help. But he knew it would also arrest his thoughts. For the time being, he believed that reminiscing would ease the pain. Afua would only be critical. She would be very critical and hence derail the whole process of thought and healing.

****

"My job involves cutting-up potatoes in a factory. Look Afua, that job has crippled my spine. Afua, I've all the answers now," Ko-Ofie said aloud, and then paused with the realization that Afua might hear him. Ko-Ofie peered through the doorway and mumbled, "It's wrong Afua. Yes, I've found the answer. Yes, I've answers!

Then Ko-Ofie paused, took the end of his shirt, and wiped off sweat on his face.

"Am I disillusioned like all others? Yes, there are those who preach so much about Africa, but see nothing wrong in rejecting Africa. I cut potatoes in these parts, but would never do it in Ghana. There are African men who clean-up white men in these parts and proudly call it a job and earning-a-living. But the same African men would not even clean-up their children in Africa."

Ko-Ofie sat down and clasped his face in his hands.

Raising his head, he whispered, "They prefer to say that I've been in these parts for twenty years. None ever says I've belonged to these parts for twenty years!"

****

He wiped off sweat on his forehead and undid all the buttons on his shirt.

****

91

In order to gain applause during academic presentations at African Studies conferences organized by white scholars inany corner of the world, African scholars must quote white Africanists at length. There should also be a mouthful of nasalized tones based on the Victorian pronunciation, or arecourse to the American slang and twang.

****

Occasionally, in order to promote their knowledge, African scholars who ply their trade in these parts are invited to give lectures on the dangers of dug-out latrines in Africa. And theircomparative perspectives are always harvested from ancient latrines in these parts. On such occasions, African scholars compare latrines in Africa with Roman latrines, Greek latrines, Victorian latrines, Hapsburg latrines, Harappan latrines, and so on. This is the hallmark of educated Africans: always prefacingwhatever they write with the perspectives of ancient white writers. Shakespearean lines come in handy and are applauded. Thucydides! Socrates! Name them. Even editors of academic journals require African scholars to quote extensively from frameworks theorized by white scholars. Write on the Asante Empire. Your key is Ivor Wilks. Never seek to use Kwame Arhin! Ah! The best comes from the West. This nursery rhyme has gained deep roots in the world.

****

A restrained smile took hold of Ko-Ofie's face, and he barely whispered, "Even in the academic field of dug-out latrines, Africans compare theirs with those of whites and assume that the white ones are better."

****

And the educated African elites are not only imitating their white counterparts. There is another spiral. Bereft of how to rescue Africa in the hegemonic hands of the white specialists on Africa, the educated African elites take the alternative to joinlocal politics, or the so-called democratic dispensations. And you have them all over place. Ah! Doctors and Professors in every nook and corner of the political corridors. They are the pen-armed robbers. Some call them the "Stealers!" Their craft is about using their knowledge to wield the pen to rob the nation and its citizens. In some cases, the educated pen-armed robbers obtain their doctorate degrees from backyard universities in these parts. Today, African politicians are buying degrees fromdiploma mills in these parts. The educated pen-armed robbers' ideologies constitute desperate politics, sporadic salvationist ethics, mutated progress, and above all, getting rich overnight for no work done.

****

Ko-Ofie thought about returning home to join local politics.But what comes with being a returnee depressed him. It is not an idea he wanted to entertain. Besides, politics, there was no potato factory. And he feared being a subject of mockery in Ghana as much as Afua had mocked him as a PhD-holder who was a "potato-cutter" in these parts. Well, he could set up his own potato factory. But he knew he was already seventy-seven years late laboring in these parts. Time was not on his side. Besides, he had heard about numerous cases of Ghanaian professionals who returned home to work. They were victimized by Ghanaians based in Ghana who were not willing to consider new ideas, or saw them as a threat to the positions they held.

****

There are also the returnees or been-tos. These are former velvet seekers. They are the living ancestors and local gods. They are worshipped not revered. They are worshipped daily. Yet, they are not the gods of yesterday. Their ritual attributes are easier to grasp. They include defaced gold watches and embroidered dog chains, star spangled embossed winter boots, cars with perennial foreign number plates of these parts, balding permed hair or traces of it, bleached skin or its darkened vestiges, and speech that cracks through the nostril. Some of these returnees are anemic in grammar and boast of what they call American slang. The paradox is that they may have been velvet seekers in the Ukraine but happen to speak with evanescent neo- Americanized accents!

****

Yet, another group is the waiters. The waiters encourage the departees who eventually become velvet seekers to do their best to harvest the cargoes that are needed by the waiters. Thus,the waiters put pressure on the velvet seekers to ensure that the latter return home with the velvets, the prized paraphernalia of the Church of the Cargo-Cult of Africa.

****

No doubt, the waiters are the sages of modern Africa. Their best saying is that "When you are in Rome do as the Romans do!" They don't know that velvet seekers are never consideredas Romans. Therefore, even if they do as the Romans do, they would still appear strange to and excluded by the Romans! Thewaiters have the will-power to dream. They have the courage and belief to wait for the return of the departees. The waiters thrive on the dreams of waiting for the ritual return of the departees. More importantly, they also hope that one day they will leave as departees and become velvet seekers. And on suchdays, they will also have glamorous waiters. There is a linearityto it. But when the departees return home, it becomes cyclical journey that sweeps up both velvet seekers and waiters in the whirlwind of the Church of the Cargo-Cult of Africa.

The departees parade African airports with their shoulders raised high and stiff as in death. Their acquisition of Euro- American accents and mannerisms begin at African ports of departure. The African airports are the majestic sites of funeralceremonies for all departees who will be the living dead in these parts in the future. Also the departees take part in the ritualized messages of miragic African renaissance of the sacredmaterialistic cult of the living dead.

Parts of a departee's fortunes of traveling to these parts are cherished by the waiters. And grandparents, and parents, uncles and aunts, cousins, nephews and nieces, brothers and sisters, and all those who can claim any form of kinship with the departee, have to be at the port of departure for the farewell ceremony for the living dead. It is the dying aspect that yields rebirth in mundane materiality. It is a ritual that all family members pray for and revere. These constitute the new eschatology of Africa. It is the new death of both the young andthe old. The departees, the new velvet seekers, are not judged, provided that their velvets arrive before their death. The burial of a velvet seeker is simply a means to send him or her awayso that his/her velvets will be inherited by the living dead: the waiters. This is a sacrosanct part of the new African eschatology.

Departees swagger in Victorian second-hand woolen suits in the temperamental

African heat. There are those with leather jackets imported from Hong Kong, Malaysia, Cambodia, and Taiwan. Such jackets are specially made for Africans who are ever ready to buy the products of others, but their own. There are praise songs for the Victorian woolen suits and the Hong Kong leather outfits. And much will be said about the length and breadth of a departee's coat long after the departure. And the texture of one's woolen trousers is not left out! A pair of shoes should be a second-hand Italian-made one. Locally made shoes never get to reach African ports of departure. Hand gloves and ties, especially, bow-ties are a status symbol. All these point to the fact that the African traveler happily goes through the mill of Westernization long before the departure.

It is better if the departee belongs to a family of deceased velvet seekers. The departure is surely to be graced with relics of the dead. Such relics include old air fare tickets, British Airways' cigarette lighters, Swissair's paper plates, KLM's plastic cups, Aeroflot's maps, and Air Canada's pens. Above all, American Airlines key-holders, indeed, any souvenir from the US of A! These and others are necessary, if a departee wants to have uncountable waiters to send him or her off to the province of the living dead in these parts.

Departees are expected to change their accents during the rituals of departure. They should divert speech through the nose. And African names should be altered. All names that reflect the assumed African flair for jawbreaking names should be abandoned for Elizabethan ones. Better still, such names should have Hollywoodized flamboyance: Tess and Tessie! Anna and Anne! Joe and Jee! Ree and Ray, and of course, RIP and Rip Van Winkle! Dan, Don or Don Quixote! And the pronunciation of such hallowed names should fit the celebrated white accents.

****

These are aspects of the worldviews and ontologies that informceremonies at African ports of departure for the living dead in these parts.

****

Sweat poured from Ko-Ofie's forehead. And he touched his armpit and it was very wet. He felt sweat pouring down his back too. He felt dizzy. He shook and raised his over-flooded head to look up at the gold-embroidered clock that had alwaysindicated the hour. He was not so much concerned with the passing time. It was what life in these parts was inflicting and Africans that concerned him.

But there was something to the passing time. Although undefined, Ko-Ofie knew that his own life shaped it. It offered it life in those areas where there was none.

Ko-Ofie spoke softly to himself, "It's simple. So long as we seeksalvation in these parts, Africa will be blurred in the global mirror of life. Our marginalization as a people in the shit-holes of these parts will continue. It's inexorable, pure and simple."

Pausing, Ko-Ofei looked around as if he was addressing a captive audience, and then whispered quietly, "Now, do I belong to the class of the haves in these parts?"

Then, there was a whisper within. It was clear and lucid. But the beating of his heart frustrated its essences and nuances, turning it into a whimpering nothingness.

At least, despite Afua's accusations, he knew he possessed all the cargoes that Africans are looking for both in these parts and in Africa where the waiters are poised like hunting lions. The materiality of the cargo-cult includes television, IPods, IPads, computers, fridge, VCR and Italian shoes. Of course, lately the waiters look up to Japanese chop sticks and Kentucky Fried Chicken which they proudly called KFCee! Above all expensive cars. These days a V8 vehicle crowns it all. It has a political poise to it. Ah! The days of Mercedes Benz and BMW are over. Range Rover. They call it "Rainage." These are the new class determinants in Africa. And it's the law. It's no longer the norm or social expectation.

And all returnees need to show samples of the cargo-cult mentality. Japanese TV! Italian shoes! German Mercedes Benz! British Range Rover! Americanized violence if not Ford and slang! Danish pornography! Chinese umbrellas! French tea cups or fashion pictures! And of course, Russian vodka if a returnee wishes to visit any palace.

****

As these thoughts drained Ko-Ofie, his heart pounded his chest cavity. It was nothing new. Afua had said on numerous occasions, "You are dead, Ko-Ofie." The message is simple: he will return to Ghana as a living-dead. His final place! The resting place! The place of his actual death! And the place of his final burial! The essences of the new African eschatology are built around the acquisition of the velvet, the key route to the cargo-cult.

****

The waiters revere white people of these parts who parade their sanguinary wares in Africa. They include sexual predators, political propagandists, economic exploiters, errant academics, NGO-officers, sex tourists, and gold predators, mostly Chinese, called Galamsey. These represent the former cultural eccentricities of colonial missionaries and teachers. The missionary work is not over. The political tutelage is not over. The survey of gold-bearing regions is not over. The colonial liturgies continue. And it is called neocolonialism.

****

The new missionaries of neocolonialism are now African governments. They are also pen-armed robbers. They use pens and ordinary paper as their equipment of robbery.

African leaders are assisted by ministers also sometimes known as secretaries or commissioners. These are the doctrinaire teachers that assist the new missionaries. Some ministers of state are erstwhile self-acclaimed Marxist scholars who had preached morality to previous governments. But once they enter into politics, they abandon all traces of morality and transparency. Their new ideological vocation is to steal as much resources of the state as possible.

****

The pen-armed robbers are trained in the universities. Every student is carefully put through the pen-armed robbery training based on some materialistic curricula of social mobility to be derived from public and civil service. But the beneficiaries are mostly members of National Union or Association of Students and Student Representative Councils. These two bodies are corrupted on university campuses before they join the public or civil service. They are hired by politicians to do their bidding on campuses. Stolen money from state coffers is thrown before student leaders during local and national elections to buy votes on behalf of politicians. Having already tasted money on campuses, they join political parties after graduation not to serve the nation, but to steal from the nation. They graduate from universities in slim physical structures. But within months of joining politics, they grow big bellies! These are the potential leaders of

Africa. Graduates schooled in the art of pen-armed robbery.

****

The new missionaries and their teachers are supported in many ways by the headquarters of the former colonial missionaries. Hence, the new missionaries can afford to throw religious parties with state funds. Such religious parties are a part of thenew religions in Africa. They depend on the new missionaries who feed from the fountains of the old missionaries.

The political associates of the new missionaries are multinational corporations, assisted by foreign scholars from these parts. These are the agents that feed the new missionaries with answersto their political and economic problems. Development with foreign aid is placed under the auspices of young white collegegraduates of these parts. Such college graduates have one thinggoing for them in their dealings with the new missionaries. They bristle with white supremacy of these parts. For the greater part of their education, these twenty-one year-old white graduates are taught that all of Africa is the Serengeti. It is full of lions and tigers. They are trained to think that Africa is Somalia and Somalia is Africa. It is full of infinite hunger and political chaos. All of Africa is the Congo. It is full of warfare. And allof Africa is riddled with endemic hunger, disease, and death. This knowledge is limitless. And upon graduation they call it

"Specialization Certificates & Degrees in African Studies."

****

Ko-Ofie got up from the armchair and paced the room. Suddenly, he stopped and began to roam about in the room. He remembered it. It was a newspaper cutting showing the new missionaries in Africa. He stopped roaming and briefly called Afua.

Afua responded and asked, "What has come over you! Why are you moving about aimlessly?"

"I'm looking for my newspaper cuttings that deal with the BODAM DAMS. Remember those with the ministers shaking hands with white high school math teachers."

"And what's it about the newspaper cuttings?"

"I want to read them all over again!" Ko-Ofie paused and continued, "Remember the white math teachers are twenty- year old graduates. They were sent from these parts to Ghana to evaluate the viability of new hydro dams being built in Ghana."

Ko-Ofie paused and looked at Afua who was moving to the kitchen!

Afua turned around, and wearing a sympathetic face, remarked, "What has come over you?"

****

Ko-Ofie did not provide any answer. He pulled out a drawer and brought out some newspaper cuttings. One had the caption:

EUROPA-AMERICUS HIGH SCHOOL MATHEMATICIANS TO EVALUATE THE BODAM DAMS IN GHANA

All the new missionaries of state were present. They were flanked by nubile and virile girls with their ritualized succulent breasts, all to the world. Such ceremonies go uncompleted without the portrayal of waist beads and breasts, grass-made skirts, daggers and dancing. That is the African culture portrayed to visiting foreign dignitaries. In this instance, white high school math teachers who had been paid by the big bank of the world to supervise the building of the Bodam Dams, feasted their eyes on succulent black breasts. Such illustrates the putative celebration of festivals and ceremonies of indigenous ritual performance. And these staged festivals have no value to the event at hand. Hence, they only express, champion, and affirm the lurid primal values associated with Africa in these parts. And these images come in the form of sun, sin, and sex.

****

Ko-Ofie imagined the number of clicking cameras and how photos of succulent-breasted, innocent Ghanaian girls would cross the Atlantic and the Pacific. And the pictures would be flashed in the front pages of newspapers. The pictures would serve as appetizers for six o'clock TV news heard and viewed around gregarious dinner tables in these parts. The pictures would soon be the subjects of anthropological discussions during Africa studies conferences. Some men from these parts would resurrect faith in their limping libidos by admiring the exotic African women. And above all, the pictures would signify a part of the construction of the BODAM DAMS.

****

The opening address for the ceremony to commemorate the BODAM DAMS was read by the MINISTER OF SCIENTIFIC AND CULTURAL DEVELOPMENT. A local newspaper has it that he had a PhD from Europa-Americus Academy of Sciences in BODAM ENGINEERING.

But the BODAM DAMS have a religious dimension to them: they re-open the Atlantic Middle Passage. It is a reminder that the Atlantic route is still open. The dehumanization and marginalization of Africa still exist. And there is an analogy that is interesting. It is a simple factual analogy. Perhaps, misplaced but it makes sense: Africans are now air-lifting themselves to these parts. It is a relentless quest, an inexorable pernicious cycle of African servitude.

****

These parts are the places of death before sickness. They are the places where BODAM DAMS are planned before constructing them in Africa. The torture of the soul goes on without death! And it is where the paralysis of the body occurs without death! These parts are the places of the living-dead Africans.

****

Ko-Ofie felt numb in the chest and heavy in both feet. He crouched and leaned against the wall. But he realized he couldnot stand on his feet. Bracing the window panes, he squinted through the window. The moon maintained its distance in the discriminatory, cloying evening sky. And as he opened his eyes, the moon had drifted away, blurring in the distance. He touched the wall for something to support himself. There was nothing to hold onto. All was flat. Everything became blurred like the far away moon. He clutched onto the curtains. Then, the distant moon and the smog-entombed neon-lit surroundings gave way to utter darkness.

Afua heard some noise. Pieces of broken glass were on the floor. Ko-Ofie lay on the floor, oblivious of his broken, but glittering surroundings. Afua made for the phone. The wailingof a hospital ambulance registered in the distance. Eclipsing the familiar and disturbing cringing industrial noise, the ambulancearrived.

Chapter Five

Afua moved about in the shopping mall. Suddenly, she was struck by the radiant presence of a young man. And instantly, the young man began to glide away like a rainbow. There was an apparent mirth in what he was doing. He was looking around and smiling at no one in particular.

The young man turned around to face Afua's direction. Their eyes met and he smiled at her. But she could not smile back; she was apparently dazzled by his confident, self-assured bearing.

For the first time in many years, here was an African in these parts whose smile radiated from within! It came from the innersprings of his soul. Afua knew that the young man was wearing the smile of someone who had waited for the actualization of the African dream: the quest for the velvet in these parts. He was celebrating his quest for the velvet. His smile had all the signifiers of the inner joy of the newly-arrived velvet seekers in these parts.

Afua was convinced that the young man's smile was a product of the new African communal dream. The dream is about coming to these parts. Some people call it coming to America. It is the dream that presages the acquisition of the velvet.

****

Mesmerized by the cargo-cult goods in the store, the young man waltzed with the shopping cart, raised an eye here, threw an arm there, and appeared to be shuffling his feet to the beat of the wheels of the shopping cart!

****

"Oh, he must have really arrived," whispered Afua as her eyes followed his movements.

****

Afua belched on an acidic substance in her mouth and swallowed hard. She had taken her vitamins but had not eaten.

****

In spite of all the abundance of food in the store, Afua, like all the seasoned velvet seekers, don't feel like eating at all. Hunger in their case does not lead to yearning to eat. Rather, hunger induces pain and regret. The weekly shopping has become a ritual, in fact, a religious exercise of paying homage to the cargo-cult goods in the store.

****

Afua thought about the happiness that beclouds the newly- arrived. It is the result of many anticipated perspectives on the ways that these parts are constructed as a paradise. She could tell that the young man had just come from Ghana. It was his looks and composure that said it all. He was ruggedly handsome, unlike those seasoned velvet seekers, who have beenlong entombed and made wretched by these parts. Also, there was something enthralling about him that the matured velvet seekers lacked: he appeared like someone who did not know where he was, but was sure of himself and felt comfortable with the mere presence of his being that he had arrived.

****

The young man's composure was certainly the result of a culmination of a long dream. It was obviously a long-awaited dream! His arrival in these parts was a victory for his family and society, in fact, all those who had helped in making his dream a reality. And so his composure seemed to be telling and celebrating some long-entertained achievements.

****

Afua was reminded of the story about the aged and death.On the verge of dying, the aged exhibit the best enthusiasm to embrace death. It is always a realization that death reunites them with their departed loved ones. The process of dying is a long journey. It summons the physical and ethereal presenceof the dying and the dead. During the journey to the world of the beloved ancestors, the place of the living is also important. The living stands to gain in the process if the meeting between the dying person and the dead is cordial. Such meetings are preparations for the living people's own future development.

****

The crossing from Africa to these parts is also another form of living death. Afua's own experiences in the international airports of these parts provide examples of the rigors and humiliations of the journey, especially, the anatomical searches.

****

The white female immigration officer began with a furtivesmile and proceeded to officially search Afua by inserting her clinically gloved fingers into Afua's womanhood. The officer smirked and moaned. Deeper and deeper she pushed her middle finger. Afua screamed, and as she did so, the white lady's body was rocked slightly with a gust of hegemonic immigration satisfaction.

"Oh, you've really come," moans the white lady.

"Yes, I come from Ghana. Believe me, there's nothing, in fact, nothing in there. I put nothing there. Whatever, I've is in my bag," Afua replied.

"Well, we've to search you in there," said the white immigration officer, as she pointed to Afua's genitalia area.

The white immigration officer chuckled and continued, "Some of you hide cocaine and other contraband goods in that female compartment. But, there is something I need to tell you. You are very neat and smell good in there."

Finally, the white lady, ritually, in fact, in a well-practiced manner, put her middle finger, the one that had just explored the contours of Afua's traumatized womanhood for cocaine, into her salivating mouth.

"You're very sweet in there, very very sweet and neat in that cavity. Over here," the white lady commanded and pointed to the direction which Afua should go.

The white lady felt contended with the search. She would always have a field day. She would continue to access the salubrious cavities of African womanhood for contraband goods.

****

There are other things that pertain to the airports of these parts that involve subtle searches and queries: facial scrutiny, search for "tribal" origin, state affiliation, and political ideologies. Also, there are subtle HIV/AIDS evaluations, assessments of hunger, diseased bodies, and civil war and warlike proclivities.

****

In contrast, policies at African airports are different and well- packaged to receive foreigners, especially light-skin visitors. The lighter you are the easier it is to gain entry. At African airports, if you happen to be lighter in complexion, "me broni,"or my "white lord," as Ghanaians happily say, you have free and unencumbered entry. As long as a visitor wears a light skin, African immigration officials would not ask for country oforigin, would not ask about immunization, and would not ask about the purpose of entry or visit. And so daily we worship "me broni" even when we know that they are in our country toengage in terrible things like child sex and pornography!

****

Suddenly, feeling tired and weak, Afua stepped out of theshopping mall. She sat on a bench in the corridor of the shoppingmall. She looked around. The mall was full of human activity, yet as usual devoid of humanizing.

****

Afua recollected her thoughts. It didn't make sense. The comparison was too obscure. It couldn't be death in both cases. She pondered, "No African comes to these parts to experience both life and death at the same time. But they end up being theliving-dead. Death has too many meanings for Africans in theseparts: the most harrowing one is the living-death syndrome that presages the actual death."

****

"Why do we keep coming to these parts? This time without force, in new slave vessels that fly across all oceans? And why has the young man also come to these parts? These time there is no pernicious gun-slave-cycle that support any Triangular Trade. Is it all about acquiring visas to board flying slave vessels, or walking across the Sahara to reach the Mediterranean coast?"

****

"Oh! Oh! Why do I speak to myself like Ko-Ofie?" Am I also getting sick?"

****

"Well, at least I know of the sufferings that entomb Africans in these parts. After all home is home. The fact is that we've got it all wrong. Why can't we develop our Africa? Of course, a few dollars and Euros in these parts elevate us above the so- called poverty at home." Afua pondered, whispered "poverty," wiped off sweat on her forehead, and returned to the mall.

****

The young man was at the far corner of the store, crouched over some items. He examined one item after another, as if he had seen all before somewhere, or heard a lot about them, but never touched any before.

There was freedom and fluidity in his movements. He was like a dammed river that had broken its banks, flowing in a vast uncharted valley, where swaggering emanated from graceful movements.

Thinking that that the young man was enchanting, Afua held her breath as her prying gaze traveled to his immaculate hair. It was beautiful, raw and luxuriantly rich.

Afua closed the distance between her and the young man, and another thing struck her. The color of his skin shone and rippled. It was fresh, vibrant and inviting.

Then, Afua stole a quick glance at her own fingers. There was a great difference. There was no vibrancy in the texture of her skin. The contoured wrinkles shocked her. There was no life in it. Rather, it had vagaries of AMBI-identity.

Unsure of what she really wanted to do, Afua approached the young man and asked, "Are you from Ghana?"

Looking surprised, but undaunted, the young man answered, "Yes please, madam." "I am also from there."

The word "there" stuck in Afua's throat. It did not sound right.

There, there! Where?

Afua quickly recollected her thoughts, smiled, and asked, "What is your name? I am Afua. How long have you been here?"

Afua pushed the shopping cart closer to him. She did not want other shoppers to hear their conversation because his rough accent could betray them as Africans!

"My name is Ababi. I am a student," he

replied.

Afua watched him as he answered confidently, "I arrived only two weeks ago. This is my first shopping here. Actually, I shouldn't say I'm shopping, I'm just looking around."

"Oh you mean you're window-shopping! Where do you live?" "In an on-campus apartment!"

They exchanged telephone numbers, and Afua promised that she would invite her home for dinner.

****

Feeling a sense of pity for the innocent young man, Afua concluded that he would soon be lost to the sorrows of winter and the wizardry of summer.

****

Corruption of innocence is always swift for the newly-arrived velvet seekers. Besides, they arrive already strangled by the influence of velvet seekers, also known as been-tos or those who return to their birth-places in Africa after suffering from the pandemic of the living dead in these parts! Soon, and very soon, Ababi would experience the corrosive effects of neon lights, the inner rage that comes with racism, and the loss of the self. Then there is the rustic life to fathom. The peripheral living experiences of velvet seekers come unannounced. And one has to consider their marginalization in the mega cities of these parts, the places of their living death can be harrowing.

****

"I hate it now; I hate it in the mega cities," Afua whispered, as she pushed the shopping cart.

****

Afua hated the ritual of shopping. There was everything she could buy. Yet, she experienced regret any time she visited the shop. There was an alluring presence, yet, a sense of revulsion. Pain arose from the loss of happiness, anger from alienation, and utter loneliness from marginalization.

****

"Oh these assaults that pummel my very being," she lamented.

****

Sometimes Afua thought about the mistake she made by following Ko-Ofie to these parts. Ko-Ofie had explained to the waiters, the devotees, and worshippers of the velvet, including her parents, that these parts were full of life.

****

And yes, Ko-Ofie had described these parts as a place of mega-cities. True, it was, in

116

graphic contrast to where she had experienced her formative years. But whose definition of cities anyway! If the contrast is based on environmental factors, then the so-called mega cities of these parts are doomed-cities of hell. And whose concept of civilizations was Ko-Ofie talking about?

Civilization in these parts and the otherizing! The criminality! The individualism! The hypocrisy! The violence! The loneliness! The old people's homes where they go to die! And love for dogs instead of fellow human beings! The love for guns for killing fellow human beings! Children in schools are killed! Mass murders in restaurants! Killings in Church! Mass killings in shopping malls! Targeted killings at political rallies! Salacious murders in homily settings. They sanitize all in these parts. They call it the civilization of the gun.

****

Civilization! African intellectuals, both at home and in these parts, have embraced the images of doom, moral decay, warfare, chaos, and violence that have come to be associated with infant Africa.

African intellectuals, especially those in these parts, live on the edges of synchronized frustration. And there are so many of them, all velvet seekers. They wear prostheses of happiness, augment their laughter, wear wide grins, and speak with affected accents. They hide their pain and anguish. Behind the pain and anguish is a fortress that has been

117

constructed for them by the decision makers of these parts.

****

Afua thought about how Africans now are eager to travel beyond the seas to these parts. Answers are difficult to find. However, those like her, who occasionally return home are notoffered the opportunity to tell the truth about their sufferings in these parts. Rather, people like her are worshipped because they have returned with temporary cures for Africa's ailment: dollars, Euros, and Yen. The cures are couched in cargo-cult mentality. In the end, the concocted stories that ooze from the mouths of velvet seekers have found resting places in the heartsof children. Thus, both children and adult think that these parts are full of sweets, toffees, coca cola, cars, Superman, and aboveall, Tarzan striding the US of A. Yes, the US of A, the home with the dollar embossed with "In God We Trust," but where ungodly democracy of racism is practiced with glee.

****

During one of Afua's most recent visit to Ghana, a child had asked her whether she lived in the Empire State. The child, who called himself Johnny Empire State, had asked about the latest and the most beautiful building she saw before returning home.Afua had thought that the child would allude to the beauty, but not the complexity of the building. So insistent was Johny Empire State that he attracted the attention of a circus of children around Afua. In the end, Afua was forced to say the Sky-dome in Toronto was the most beautiful building in the world she hadseen. A din broke out as the children tried to outperform one another in order to take on that name.

Finally, a stout boy shouted and it was echoed by all the rest "Call me SEKODOMEY, SEKODOMEY."

The echoes took over the serene, moon-lit night. Shadows of raised hands of chapped happiness, acknowledging the new name, eclipsed the mooring moon-lit night.

Afua closed her eyes and held her hands to her ears for sometime.She wanted to tell them about the homeless, the hungry, the unclothed, those who inject themselves with medicines in order to get sick, countless rapes, incest, adultery, drugs, horrendous murders, cannibalism, dirt and decay of the human soul, nepotism, political corruption, corrosive competitiveness, racism and all. And something they call one-parent family And yes, clearly defined residential areas for the poor, the rich,blacks, and whites.

****

Powerful as these images were, Afua knew it: had she told them about the suffering in these parts, she would have been considered the killer of the African children's dream. The children would not understand. After all, she had never understood it herself.

119

Had she told them, she would have beenthe killer of the communal African dream. They would foreverconsider her as the selfish one. She would have obstructed the inexorable flow of the historical links between Africa and theseparts. She would have been blamed for cutting the umbilical cords between the glories of these parts and the decaying Africa that has always needed help from foreign midwifery.

The SEKODOMES AND JOHNY EMPIRE STATES are blinded before their journey into the world of the elements of these parts. They are forever blindfolded in this life. Such childhood blind-folding has been celebrated for centuries. In some coastal polities, the Afro-European encounter is over four hundred years old. Yes, the Fantes may even boast that their contact with Europe is one thousand years old. The irony is that the Wassa, the Efutu, the Agona, the Ahanta, the Nzima, and the Denkyira, all those who have some geographical affinity with the Fantes, the beneficiaries of the corrosive mutative Afro- European culture, claim some Fanteness! And it is the loss of African culture. And it is simply the quest for the West. It is as simple as that. Remember the nursery rhyme: the best comes from the West. No questions asked!

CALL ME SEKODOMEY! It means something else. It is the essence of the new eschatology. It is calm and sometimes warm. It is a new lifestyle full of decay. It is for a meretricious adaptation. But above all, it is relentless. Steps toward debilitation, decay, and living death.

****

Afua looked around to make sure that she was not all alone in her movements in the world of inexorable self-enslavement. But she was all alone. All by herself! Alone and marginalized! She was hounded by a sea of a rippling wave of white faces. And then the pangs of pain drowned her. It was the bitterness of knowing that she was a part of the all- knowing, but tongued- tied velvet seekers.

****

Velvet seekers who return to their places of birth are never heard. They refuse to explain that food is available but they are unable to eat it. And that freedom in these parts is a mirage. That these parts are a police state: litigants' haven built on materialism! Freedoms are constrained by limited happiness, circumscribed by criminal acts, and encased in collective morbidity. TV news and TV dramas glorify murderers. And there are old people, known as SENIOR CITIZENS, dumped in marginalized flower-entombed homes. They sit on their sore buttocks until loneliness, sorrow, and death take them captives. This is their world of civilization. It is a world where all OTHERNESSES emanate and where Africans seek their living death. And oh the "senior" does not confer any seniority on those citizens categorized as such. It simply means discarding the aged. Very soon Africans will celebrate Senior Citizens' Day!

And oh, there are fathers who sleep with both their wives and children to excite their fatherhood. Lovers who force their partners to eat their shit as an integral part of loving and eatingit all! Making love to horses, pigs, dogs and all.

These aberrations never cross the Atlantic to Africa. They are not known beyond the Pacific. And the Mediterranean, knownfor its fury of keeping Africans back, is also silent when it comes to these perennial problems inherent in the civilizations of theseparts.

****

Afua pushed her shopping cart to the cashier's counter and paid for the items. The store, the shopping malls, and all other areas of capitalist enterprise are the best places to experience momentary happiness, association, and communality in these parts. They are better than many places, including her home. At least, in the stores, the salespersons and cashiers smile at customers as if for centuries they have been their friends. But there is also something strange about their smiles. Once, a customer pays for the items that s/he has purchased, there is a follow-up custom, and it is very simple. With a well-manufactured smile, the salesperson should announce, "There you go." And of course, off you go.

****

Walking out of the store, Afua began to descend the staircaseto the parking lot. She steadied herself in order to maintain her balance as the bags of grocery affected her sense of gravity.

There were many white people around her. They were smartlydressed, but a shadow of subdued sullenness and isolation followed in their footsteps. The air was humid and still. The stillness of the air matched the morbid movement of white people around her. It was the movement of the living-dead.

****

Afua took in a deep breath and balanced her bags of grocery.

****

"Auntie, may I help you?"

Afua turned around and saw that it was the young African man she had met in the shopping mall. Before she could answer, he took hold of three of her bags of grocery.

"Thank you," she acknowledged the help and smiled."That is okay."

"Are you going somewhere from here?"

"No, I have no place in mind. I think I will go home; I mean to school."

Afua offered to give him a ride to the campus. They sat in her car and did not talk for sometime.

It was apparent that the young man was

enthralled by the architectural features of the downtown. He kept turning his head sideways to look at buildings and items in the stores along the route.

"Did you say your name is Ababi? Do you like it here?"

"Yes, my name is Ababi" he replied, still prying into the stores, without bothering to look at Afua.

"What do you like about overseas in particular?"

Ababi looked at her and smiled, "I think everything here is okay."

Afua smiled back and continued, "Is it the way you imagined before coming to these parts?"

"You know I haven't been to many places here, but at least I'm impressed."

"What has impressed you the most? Is it anything in particular?

Ababi smiled again, and this time did not volunteer any answer.

Afua realized that Ababi was not ready to answer the question and hence quickly asked him what he had bought at the grocery store.

"I bought milk, bread, and eggs," he smiled and added, "Those are all that I bought, and I guess they are what I need for now.""Would those be sufficient enough for the week?"

"Yes, I also eat from the dining hall. Oh, I mean the student cafeteria!"

Afua drove on. Silence momentarily took over. She calculated that Ababi was about twenty-six years old. Also, she realized that he was not prepared to be chatty. Perhaps as a

Ghanaian, he had already considered her as an older person who deservedrespect.

Breaking the silence, Afua asked, "So have you eaten any African, oh, I mean Ghanaian food, since coming here?"

"No, I haven't and I miss my Ghanaian food."

"Well, then come home with me and eat fufu. To be sure it is not like the real one back home. But it is a good substitute. Youknow, some of us still treasure our local dishes."

"Oh, that will be nice, thank you," replied Ababi."Is there anything special on campus today?" Ababi looked puzzled.

"I mean do you have anything to do on campus.""No, nothing in particular," he replied.

Afua paused as if she was not sure of what she wanted to say, and said," Okay, then, home we go. You will tell me more about Ghana!"

"You mean right now."

Afua looked at him, nodded, smiled and intoned, "Not now but later."

"Please, why don't I leave my things on campus before we go to your house?"

"Okay," Afua smiled.

Chapter Six

Ababi took the bags and followed Afua.

The summer afternoon was still young. And the sun was very bright. It was as if a variegated umbrella was hanging above them.

"Why are you looking into the skies? Well, here the weather functions at two extremes: cold winters and hot summers, and we've the latter now," Afua explained.

Across the lawn were two opened doors. Their entrances revealed a large, well-furnished room, occupied by a group of white women.

Looking across from where they were standing, Afua volunteered, "Do you know what they are doing there? They are discussing their marital problems!"

"Is that so?"

"They come here every two weeks to meet with a marriage counselor," Afua continued.

"You mean there are institutions that counsel divorcees! What role does the divorced person's family play?"

"Ask me again?" Afua replied and continued, "Let us wait here for the elevator to come down."

As they waited in the lobby, they heard the on-going discussions in the well-furnished room.

There was a young white lady standing beside a large table. She was like a missing child in a market-place.

An elderly white lady of about seventy

years old beckoned to the young white lady.

Turning to the teeming divorcees, the elderly white lady focusedon the young white lady, and began to address them, "This is Nona-Married Maturity. She has a B.A. in psychology and she specializes in marriage counseling. This is a landslide victory for us, divorcees. We got the expert we wanted."

Pausing and smiling, the elderly white lady, surveyed her audience for an approval, and continued, "Nona-Married is only twenty-one years old and recently became engaged to herchildhood sweetheart. You all know what I'm talking about andhow it feels like."

The elderly white lady adopted a posture of seriousness and continued, "In fact, I mean it when I say that we're lucky. Nona-Married has the experience; she's read many books on marriage. In short, she's a recognized authority in the field of counseling divorcees. Her appointment is for five years."

Turning, to Nona-Married, the elderly white lady curtsied and said, Ms. Maturity, we're forever your clients. Thank you."

The old lady asked the audience of divorcees to introducethemselves. From the introduction their ages ranged between eighteen and seventy-plus, and all were going throughtraumatic divorces.

"Would you like to marry one of them?" Afua jokingly asked.

"Ha, I am not interested in divorcees."

"Afua sizzling with laughter, cleared her throat, and said, "You know that's the opening line of African men. Very soon I shall find you with a "Darkie mfa nko." Ha, that's only when the color complex works in favor of fat and old white women."

"What's "a darkie mfa nko"?"

"Oh, you don't know! They're old, or fat, or perennially divorcedwhite women, who find sanctuaries of love and solace with you African guys. I'm sure you will get one soon!"

"But you can't lump all African men together!"

"Please, let me finish what I've to say, may be you will get to know whether you belong to the lump or not."

"Sorry! Go ahead and finish it then; I'm listening."

"Okay, invited guests," Afua giggled, "Oh the color complex has affected your minds for so long. And yes, the patriarchal and racist, social structures of these parts restrict you, I mean African men, from dating their young and pencil-slim white women. Ha, ha, the societies of these parts shun its overweight and older white women. This makes it possible for you, hey onemore time, let me emphasize this: you African men, to date, the ostracized overweight and older white women."

"It's not only African men who do that? What about African women?"

"Well, African women do it too! Ha ha! Aha, here it comes! Well,since day one of the contact between white and black, the white man has always been portrayed as the peerless human being."

"Oh! Please don't say that."

"What else is there to say? An African man instead? Let me finish, yeah! I was saying some

Africans, call them black women, sleep with white men just to have fair-skinned babies!"

"Are you sure about this?" It is good for race relations.

Laughing, Afua replied, "Yes, that's the more reason why I want you to marry one of those divorcees. You won't do that at home, I guess."

"I wouldn't know about that," replied Ababi, without removing his focus on the assembled divorcees.

"So what do you know?"

Ababi laughed and retorted, "I don't understand what you mean."

"Hmm! Now getting to know you. You're like all the rest. You refuse to understand simple things."

****

Ababi realized the discomfort in Afua's voice and decided to change the subject.

"So what do you say they are here for? To be counseled on how to remarry, or how to deal with post-divorce crisis?"

"Not that! You know divorce is a very traumatic experience. Some suffer emotional and mental breakdown and need to get on with their lives. Counseling alleviates the pain and trauma. I hear it helps. You see, the young lady wearing the pony tail," Afua pointed at the young white lady who had been introduced, and said, "She is the counselor."

"Yes. I heard the introduction," replied Ababi, as he continued to gaze at the young white lady.

Afua noticed that shock was written all over Ababi's face.

As their eyes met, Ababi looked down and seemed to have something on his mind. He muttered something, but Afua didn't hear it, hence asked, "What did you say?"

"Nothing, I was just wondering how this young woman, I mean how this young lady can advice these older and more apparently experienced ladies. So what about male divorcees"

Afua giggled and replied, "I guess it is paper work, you know paper qualification, I should say. The subject of male divorcees is another issue altogether"

Ababi laughed and said, "Hmmm! Well, the divorce rate in Africa is also growing, though we are yet to have ten-year olds as marriage counsellors. But we Africans love to imitate foreign things. I won't be surprised that very soon we shall abandon our norms and ask, or agree with the IMF to hire for us at our expense white marriage counsellors like the lad who was just introduced."

"Eh! Ababi, you have great ideas oh!" Afua said, as she let go the leather hand bag on her shoulder.

Feeling more comfortable, she began to address Ababi again, "One thing you must not forget is that whether paper or book qualification, the bitter experiences of divorcees are what matter and need to be healed. Then again, I don't know whether those who study the plight of divorcees are better informed than the divorcees themselves!"

"Well, insightful," remarked Ababi.

"So are you studying psychology? May be one day you can also give us some advice," Afua laughed.

"No. I'm studying African history and culture."

"How lucky am I? You are the right intellectual! Please, providesome insights into some discussions that had occurred on a TV show."

"Well, I hope that I can be of help."

"Okay, let me ask you a question. Are foreign scholars misinterpreting African history? Is that a good question to ask?"

That much, I don't know either," replied Ababi, who continued,"You see, I'm studying African history and it is annoying to know that a few years ago, some Western scholars contended that Africa had no history! Nothing has changed much, anyway.Funny, this time around Africa is full of history. But it is the type of hegemonic history that still justifies Western supremacy and domination with African agency as a mere tokenism of scholarship."

"Is that so? That's interesting. Wow! You must be a radical. Areyou a revisionist?"

"Presently, Western scholars, the media, and international organizations are subtly justifying European dominance. They are writing about Africa from their own ideological perspectives.They are no different from the David Livingstones, the Mungo Parks, and the A.B. Ellises, who used European lenses to assessAfrica."

"That's a good point."

"Western scholars study the lives and

institutions of Africans based on archival materials that speak to European agency then claim that they have written the history of African and about Africans. And Western scholars still dictate the study of African history. Sadly, African scholars are happy to quote and reference their works because our education has taught us that the West is superior and Africa is inferior. And Africans, to show that they are educated, would preface their ideas with those of Western scholars. And we have to accept dead white men as fathers of all disciplines. Father of History! Father of Medicine! Father of Geography. They are never the fathers of genocide! They are never the fathers of predatory enslavement. They are never the fathers of wanton colonialism.

"Eh! That is a long speech! Are you then saying that experience in some matters counts more than mere knowledge based on archival sources?"

"Yes, in matters that involve the African past."

"Now let me ask you about something important," Afua paused, as a wicked smile strained the edges of her taut lips.

"Go on and ask me, but remember, it shouldn't be about marrying one of those divorcees."

"Okay, thank you for reminding me, but that's far from what I wish to ask. Well, you just made a point about foreigners writing and interpreting African history, right."

"Yes, exactly what I said."

"Does it mean that you have to be a Greek

in order to understand and write Greek history, or African history just happens to be so special?"

"That's a good question. This will merit a long discussion, in fact, a long one. But I will, here and now, briefly answer your question."

"Well, go ahead, or if you like we can discuss it when we are resting at home. Anyway, why don't you broach it now? I will like to hear you discuss it.

"Okay, I'm going to give a brief explanation. Please don't cut me off, not again."

"No I won't; I promise," Afua smiled.

"Well, well you have cut me off already. Anyway, let us look atthe various themes in African-European relationship."

"Wow, good stuff! I am sorry; just go on."

"The slave trade and its abolition, the "legitimate" trade, colonization and so-called pacification, and Euro-Christianity, are all justified in terms of avowed European interest in healing the festering sores of Mother Africa."

"Was there a Father Africa?"

"You have broken your promise; please, don't interrupt me."

"Yes sir!"

"In a nutshell, the so-called civilizing mission is still being justified by Western historians, who interpret Africa accordingto ideas fed to them from childhood."

"Hmm! Interesting oh," retorted Afua, as she winked.

"You know Afua, scholars are products of their environments, hence are compelled to look through the tinted lens of their own culture and personality."

"So what is your approach to your historical studies? Do you work with empirical data or childhood doctrines?"

"You see, I prefer to work with empiricism, but I am guided by sensitivity, balance, nuance, and objectivity that do not rest on bigoted doctrinal leanings."

"Eh! You're now discussing real history, perhaps an authentic African history at last!"

"In effect, the fact remains that African history is still young; in fact, in its infancy. Hence it is malleable to bigoted doctrinal, and if you like, ideological justifications in the hands of hegemonic scholars. On the other hand, Greek and Roman histories, for example, have passed through the stages of pruning and ideological distillation. Besides, Greek and Roman histories were glorified right from their inception. And how many African historians have specialized in Greco-Roman history?"

"Any additions"

"Yes, one can only revise the glorified Greek and Roman histories and that will be seen as a quest for scholarship. But when one rewrites African history that disputes Eurocentric accounts, it is seen as an exemplification of misplaced assertiveness."

"Does African history go through the rigors of revision?"

"Well, yes, we've a number of foreign scholars, who hide behind theories and methodologies and all that in their writing of African history. Believe me, they are even worse than the Livingstones, the Mungo Parks, and all the rest.

"Why?"

"Their methodologies are not based on empirical evidence, buton flimsy probabilities and self-induced conclusions that are derived long before they visit the archives. When questioned, they anchor themselves in semantic muddle and arithmetic games. These are what I call the new apologists."

"Wow, good history, excellent language, and an authentic overview of the new African history. Anyway, I will like to hearmore about this later.

****

What were we discussing before this lecture? Oh, was it maritalcounseling and who does it?"

"I think so; it's strange."

"Wait a minute," Afua said, "Very soon you will learn that in these parts people specialize in such matters. Old age does not count at all. You will learn soon, I hope. Well let us go. I am getting hungry now."

"What exactly do they do? I mean old folks. Do they play any significant role in society as it is in Africa?"

"Hey, it is difficult to say; I mean if you compare by using Africa, then I am afraid my personal view is that they play virtually no roles."

"Exactly, what do you mean?"

"At best, they are grandpas and grandmas in genealogical terms and during festive seasons. That's, they represent family trees. Anyway, this is my personal judgement. Wait, you've a lot to learn about these parts."

****

They approached the elevator. A white woman held the elevatordoor open for them. There were four white women and an African girl in her late teens already in the elevator.

Gazing at the white women in the elevator, the African girl languidly threw her hair backwards, some of which fell onher forehead. Using two of her fingers she adeptly tugged the misplaced tufts of artificial hair to where they belonged.

The African girl smiled at Afua and said, "Oh, this warm feelingfrom the melting dregs of the hair cream, OUT OF AFRICA, is hurting my head."

"It's really an OUT OF AFRICA experience, for it has brought you a dizzying sense of being," Afua mocked in response.

As the movement in the elevator brought the African girl closerto where Ababi stood, the scent of the cream in the African girl'shair invaded his nostrils.

Suddenly, Afua braced the left shoulder of Ababi and sneezed.

The African girl shifted her prying gaze at the white women and looked at the roof of the elevator.

Noticing Ababi's discomfort, Afua whispered, "Eight more floors to go."

One of the white women exited on the twelfth floor, making room for the African girl, who placed her palms on the wall of the elevator and pried through its shiny reflection. The Africangirl's contorted image registered on the mirror-like wall. It was grotesque, yet disconcertingly beautiful. Preening her neck, thelong artificial locks of hair fell in their proper places. She held her nose with her thumb and middle finger, then a shadowy aquiline nose appeared on the reflective wall! Brushing a lock of artificial hair from her forehead, she smiled at her own torturedbeauty on the elevator wall.

Ababi noticed the searing eyes of the white women lacerating the African girl.

Consciously, the African girl pulled her hand away from the wall, and this time brought it closer to her eyes. Dropping her eyes from the intense gaze of the white women, the African girl raised her hands once more and murmured something unintelligible.

But Ababi overheard the African girl. It had something to do with color. He was sure that he had heard the initial words, "I'm catching up." He wanted to ask her, but admonishedhimself for thinking that she had said "I'm catching up with their white color."

Ababi kept watching the African girl as she tried to look deeper into her own variegated skin tones.

Then Ababi looked at the African girl's face, hoping to catch herattention. But the African girl's eyes were completely glued toa spot on her right hand where she continued to examine with microscopic precision.

****

Ababi's attention was interrupted by the cringing noise of the opening elevator doors.

"We're near home," Afua happily remarked, as she stepped out of the elevator followed by Ababi.

"What was it that the African girl was doing in the elevator?"

"You don't understand and I don't understand either, in fact, none of us does!" Afua paused and continued, "Ababi, I've nothing to say. I'm also a victim just as much as you. I saw it all. She only wants to belong! She wants to equate what her parents, school, television, name them, have taught her is the most beautiful. And that is being white: hair, skin, and all."

"You mean people can do that in an elevator and that African girl too!"

"I wouldn't say that she is from Africa or she is a continental African, she can be an African-Caribbean, an African-American, an African-Canadian, an African-European, an African-Asian, name them! We will continue to examine ourselves in elevators until we accept who we are. Yes, until each of us is able to accept our beautiful black color, the cuteness of our thick lips, the appealing broadness of our nose, and the gorgeous evenness of our hair."

"Afua you should have been a preacher. I'm sure about that now."

It's as simple as that! The African girl has been brainwashed about who she is. Believe me after such a clinical examination she will have to increase the quantity of the bleaching cream and the length and volume of her artificial hair. As for the quality, the competitive capitalist companies have always been responsible. And that girl is not alone, when it comes to acquiring such in large quantities!

"May be you don't apply it well," Ababi mocked, amidst laughter.

"That is not funny."

"But it's amusing! How could she do that in an elevator in thepresence of all those inquisitive, prying eyes?

"Your problem is that you don't understand.""Yes, I don't. Please educate me."

"It's the pain and anguish in trying to belong. There are many Africans in the mega-cities of these parts with white spots, footnoting their black complexion."

"What do you mean?"

"It's a complete skin-care culture. It's distinct with patched black spots around the contours of their bleached noses, eyes, ears, and necks. All are frantic efforts to belong. This is the colorcomplex. And the agents are AMBI and OUT OF AFRICA. Today, there are many creams manufactured locally in Africa. Eh! Pills too. To be a celebrity, one has to tone down theblackness of the skin to shine better in the limelight."

"Have you finished? Have you bleached your skin before?"

Ignoring Ababi's question, Afua continued "We are even bleaching the innermost parts of our thighs, for that's the

source of life. AMBI, the ever popular
AFRICANS MAY BE IMPROVED," Afua
stressed! And I hear these days, African
women take pills when they are pregnant with
the hope of giving birth to light-
complexioned babies. We have come a long
way from Black is Beautiful to Whiteness is
Supreme. What a sad journey to grab
decoloniality?"

"Are you all right, Afua?"

"Yes my Lord, but let me finish." "You
don't have to. I understand."

"The problem is that you don't
understand at all. Not at all! Please, leave me
to be. I go through such dizzying experiences
allthe time. My husband does too. You see,
we are all sick. I knowit. It's the lack of faith
in who we are and what we represent. Wefeel
we have to belong to some white world in
order to belong to this earth. Oh! I don't
know anymore. Anyway, for your
information, I've stopped using bleaching
creams."

"Why did you stop? I'm sorry."

"I will tell you another time. But
essentially, I want to be me.I want to love
myself. I don't want to hate myself. And don't
feel sorry for me. Feel sorry for those you
have left behind in Ghana. Yes, those who
think that coming to these parts is a blissful
journey to some Heaven. Tell them the
search for the velvet is a painful exercise. Tell
them we die daily. It's not some physical
death. It's the killing of the soul. Think about
the marginalization and dehumanization of
all our values. You're also a velvet seeker,

even the worse type."

"What do you mean?"

"Oh! You don't understand. You're co-opted easily, though, you may not assimilate blindly like other less educated Africans. That's what I mean. You speak their language and you have their taste. These make it easier for them to ensnare you with their net of corruption and exploitation."

"I feel terrible that you feel this way! Can't you stop all these nothings?"

"These nothings! Is that so?" No, I can't. You're like Ko-Ofie and all the rest. You don't want to accept the truth. You are always afraid. It hurts so much. Truly, you are the impotent and spineless African scholars, the killers of the dream."

"Wow! How often do you relapse into this mood?"

"You call this mood?" I call it an OUT OF AFRICA experience. I'm referring to the bleaching cream which agents like you force us to apply to the innermost parts of our African womanhood."

"Now what are you talking about? What is the meaning?" "Oh, you too don't understand! I mean what you the African men have influenced us to do, selling our souls and womanhood in the markets of these parts. Go to Amsterdam, London, Toronto, New York, Tokyo, Rome and Paris, and Dubai, and you will understand what I mean."

Ababi put down the grocery bags and put his arms around Afua, but she gently shrugged him off, and said, "Please don't touch me. Just listen to me."

Ababi replied, "Yes Madam, but you are going too far, hence I feel like comforting you."

"Well, I hope you're not mad at me. But it's also madness that comes from being OUT OF AFRICA. It's simple. Yes, very simple, indeed! The supple hairs on our male-constructed and exploited womanhood are also treated with chemicals. Any kinky hair on our womanhood is an abomination. In order to enrich the next generation of Africans, the cream has to be applied to the very source of life between our male-straddled thighs."

Ababi stopped momentarily, and said, "I'm sorry. I'm really sorry."

Afua smiled, adjusted her grocery bags, then laughed derisively, and continued, "There is enough heat there. Between our thighs, a male oven, constantly hot and inviting. Therefore, the new rebirth will manifest with our new skin color, an artificial African skin. Oh! There must be a better tomorrow for Africa's children!"

"Looking at the apparently confused Ababi, Afua perorated, "I've finished, but I can see that you're still confused. You will learn Ababi!"

****

The corridor leading to Afua's apartment was a long tunnel. It appeared deserted. It had a confluence where the roof and the floor seemed to meet. The darkness that emerged at the end of the corridor was puzzling and

143

nerve-tearing. From a distance, it appeared the wall would close in on them.

Somewhere, one heard the plaintive, whining sounds of washing machines. And the lights that reflected on the wall had its own message of doom. It was ghastly, making the corridor depressingly dark.

A chilling specter of loneliness haunted the corridor. Afua knew that Ababi was feeling it too. It was there in the very corridors of life, the very corridors of her existence. The very corridors of civilization.

"Don't be afraid, it's like that all the time. People live here; if you are lucky you meet one occasionally," Afua volunteered.

"Where do they go then? Do they live here at all?"

"Of course, they do. The simple fact is that you don't see them. I don't know my next door neighbor! Can you believe that?"

"No, but who am I to dispute that, Afua?"

"You don't have to dispute it. It's all over here."

****

In that chilly corridor, Ababi began to sweat. He felt a sense of desolation. He was on a road often used, but very unfriendly, very lonely, and even macabre in its entirety.

****

A sharp, piercing barking noise interrupted Ababi's thoughts. It came from a room adjacent to the elevator. Four or more of the barking sounds followed. Subsequently, the loud barking sounds were eclipsed by the moaning of a woman.

Afua took long strides. She wanted to keep some distance between her and the owners of those doleful barking sounds and finely tuned orgasmic moaning craft.

Ababi picked up his footsteps, and asked, "What's that allabout?"

"Someone is making love to a dog, and no pun intended""You mean a human being!"

"Yes, I mean a human being. Are you surprised?"

"So where is that civilization we hear so much about?"

"I suppose it has gone to the dogs."

"Please, be serious Afua," Ababi paused and continued, Afua smiled and said, "You know when HIV/AIDS was detected, scientists from these parts quickly climbed the ivory tower andproclaimed that it was the result of an African contact with thegreen monkey. The simple fact is that this warped notion is based on what they do with dogs, cats, pigs, horses, and other animals. You go online and check!"

Afua looked back and beckoned Ababi to hurry away from the region of the confused din of barking and moaning.

Ababi did not ask any more questions nor volunteer any information.

Neither did Afua volunteer any explanation. She was convinced that Ababi would not understand anyway. It would increase his anxiety. After all, she had seen him drink the hallucinating beauty of these parts.

All the same, Afua felt pity for Ababi! She braced up herself. She quickened her steps. The she took a quick look at Ababi, and asked, "Ababi does it feel like you are on desert? Do you think you are on vast desert? A desert that only offers the miragic images of fulfillment! "

"If you say so, Afua," Ababi intoned.

Sighing, Afua said, "I've endured this vast desert of a corridor. Yes, I have long-endured it with fear whose outcome is always empty feelings."

"I'm beginning to understand!"

****

As they approached Afua's apartment, another ear-shattering voice eclipsed the chaotic noise of washing machines. This time, Ababi recognized the voice as that of an elderly person.

The sharp edges of the voice seemed to go with an administration of pain. But the voice grew weaker and weaker as they put some distance between them and the site of the ear-shattering voice.

"It happens all the time," Afua remarked.

"What happens all the time? Do you mean the shrieking voice?"

"Yes, the shrieking voice. An elderly person is being abused."

Once again, Afua accelerated her steps. It was as if she was running away from an anticipated pain. It is the pain yet to be administered by Ababi, who might demand more explanations.

"What are you thinking about?" Afua stopped and solemnly surveyed Ababi.

"Let us go. I'm okay."

"I know. It's not the way you thought it would be. Many things in these parts will continue to be alien and superficial to you. And you know people of these parts have done very well. In fact, very, very well! For, they have managed to enslave us with lies. It's the same when they invaded Africa. And as then and now, it's the same vision of civilization, peace, serenity, progress, and development. That's why we are in this dismal corridor called civilization."

Afua swung the grocery bags about her, as she quickened her pace.

"Please, let me help you with that one," Ababi offered, as he pointed to one of the grocery bags.

"No. It's okay; you've enough already. You will learn that this is not the land of civilization, not at all. Our Africa is better. But then again, the inexorable flow of history will continue to pull us here. Unless the African elites, unless the African masses takeup their own causes, this corridor is our place of living death."

"Afua, I understand now." "It's disheartening for one to die before the actual death. But this is what's happening to us in this corridor of social death called civilization. It's the death of the spirit and the soul, although the body thrives on. You will be affected too, may be, not in this corridor, but in another one."

Afua remained glued to the spot near the doorstep of herapartment for some seconds. She looked at Ababi for sometime,as if she was waiting for clarifications and even dramatization of the incidents.

But Ababi only nodded. Perceptively, he concluded that Afua's words came from someone who had endured the pains of the journey through the corridor.

Smiling weakly, Ababi remarked, "Afua what you just said washarrowing and chilling. I wish that the masses in Africa wouldknow about this corridor."

Afua briefly stared at Ababi and put down the grocery bags.

But Ababi understood the look in her eyes. The corridor had become part of her new world of pain, anguish, and sorrow.

Afua fumbled in her handbag for her key. She opened the door. Andbefore entering, she took one last look at the corridor. She knew thenthat it was a place she would not return to in another life.

Chapter Seven

Ko-Ofie woke up on the hospital bed. Clasping his wet palms, he strained his mind to feel at home in the unfamiliar setting.

The nurses wore white caps and uniforms.

As he gradually came to, Ko-Ofie was sensitized by the noise around him. And the old dream awakened his weak presence of mind. Variations of the dream returned anytime he felt desolate. This time around the dream was about his return to the land of his birth. Yes, the birthplace of the devotees, worshipers, and waiters.

****

Having returned to Ghana several times, Ko-Ofie couldn't dissociate his mind from the images of the past. The images of those journeys kept coming back in his dreams. He lived through them daily. The guilt that came with it was sometimes suffocating.

Ko-Ofie had always wanted to tell those at home, the waiters, the devotees, the worshippers, and the homegets about the suffering in these parts. But that was not to be. None tolerated velvet seekers who recounted their experiences in negative terms. It is the new ideology, an unquestioned devotion to the cargo cult of these parts. Velvet seekers who bring out their negative experiences are seen as the killers of the universal African dream.

****

In this particular dream, Ko-Ofie encounters the homegets: they are a group of special waiters: the devotees of the cargo-cult and the worshippers of visiting velvet seekers.

****

Ko-Ofie's encounters with the homegets are always dramatizations of the past. But the homegets always remind him that the encounters are an on-going process, an unbroken process that links the present with the past. The encounters are inexorable processes are normatively narrated in the present tense.

****

Ko-Ofie's dreams have a lineal progression. His dreams always end with the death of a velvet seeker. Such deaths, however, do not end the relentless tide of the lineal progression. There is always a family member of a deceased homeget to continue the lineal progression.

****

In the dream, the homeget is as beautiful as any of the homegets. She smiled, as she explained to Ko-Ofie, "I was a teacher once, but teaching doesn't pay. Customs is where everyone wants to be. Even those who want to marry prefer their spouses to be customs officers."

Ko-Ofie asked, "What do you mean?"

"It's very simple. Have you ever encountered a customs officerand a teacher? It's very simple. A customs officer who comes into contact with you at the port of entry is able to send moneyhome as well as other things collected as bribes in a day's work."

"What about teachers?" Ko-Ofie asked, somewhat impatiently.

The homeget responded, "Teachers, on the other hand, do not come into contact with people like you at the ports of entry, the homeget explained with enthusiasm, as she looked at Ko-Ofie for further questions.

Ko-Ofie offered none, so the homeget continued, "In today's Ghana, teachers are considered penniless, hence unimportant. The paradox is that they educate those who overnight become rich known as the 'stealers' or pen-armed robbers. Thus, I use the word unimportant to mean poor and neglected teachers. Neglected in social circles because their pockets are not deep. They never get retirement packages in the form of cars! Ah! V8!"

Ko-Ofie just looked on with nothing to say.

"Ha ha haa," the homeget laughed, and continued, "Have you ever seen a teacher who has been asked to chair a church harvest? The teaching profession is worse off, no longer dignified, especially, in these corrupt, materialistic times."

"What is your point?"

"Be patient! Unlike other professionals or workers, teachers for the most part don't have access to the corridors where bribery is a cornerstone. It all comes down to state-sponsored corruption, and teachers are outsiders when it comes to that."

Ko-Ofie, apparently bemused asked, "So are you saying that teaching is for those who want to be poor?"

"Yes, a teacher can't be a millionaire. Absolutely, you know, ordinary elementary school bursars with Junior High School certificates are able to build mansions. In fact, teachers are the Earth's poverty in Ghana. The simple arithmetic is that they have nothing to steal unlike other workers," the homeget emphatically explained.

"Does it then mean that corruption is now a national pastime?"

"Yes it is. It is state-sponsored. If you don't steal chunks of the national cake from your workplace, you are considered a fool.

"Really, are you serious?"

"Indeed, it is the norm. It is the order of the day. And the stealing comes in many forms from all sectors of society."

"Hmm! Let me say that's some information," Ko-Ofie commended.

Smiling, the homeget explained further, "Well, I will say that is modern Ghana oh. If you steal from the state, you can be sure of a decent state funeral and burial. In fact, the more you steal, the better your prospects for a pageant state burial. Also seasoned bureaucratic thieves, known as "stealers" and pen-armed robbers, who build houses, have illegitimate kids, and control the police in their districts, have their names immortalized in living memory by having streets and avenues named after them."

"So these are now new norms!"

"Oh, yes, ask customs officers! They will tell you all about their careers. I know one who was a principal of a training college. You know, teaching does not pay. She was called Teacher Ohianior Auntie Poor T. And I was called such names too. Who would like to be told in the face that she or he is poor?"

"What did she do then? And you too?"

"Ask again! She saw newly-appointed customs officers build houses, buy cars, and change clothes like chameleons in a variegated terrain."

"Chameleons, I see."

"No one bothers to ask customs officers and their kind about the sources of their wealth and their sudden affluent lifestyles. The masses know that customs officers have made it from stealing from the state, but accept it as though that is the right thing to do."

"Is that so?"

"Don't pretend! Wait until you see and hear it all. It's not only custom officers who are stealing from the state. Name them! Bank officials get their 10 percent of loans granted to their customers. Medical, pharmaceutical, and nursing officers have their aspirin quotas. The police get their two cedi notes for stopping vehicles. And judges have their goat quotas. We have parliamentarians whose main interests in politics, or their visions of the betterment of the state, are IMF-acquired TOYOTA, PAJEROS, BMWs, and NIKE shoes and Chinesechopsticks. And oh, senior government officials have official garden-boys, washermen, and cooks. And remember the political pornographers called the press, also known as 6 o'clock news, or the Inky Fraternity, have their quotas defined by their selectivity of news items if one pays for it. And they call it soli!"

"What about the homegets and why do you call yourselves homegets?"

The homeget smiled, showing all her thirty-two teeth, and said, "Homeget is not one particular person or gender. It involves all those who grab what people like you bring from overseas, oh, you call it these parts. These days our politicians are the targeted group. They are rich. If you want to be rich immediately after university education, join politics. You people don't have the means to travel as often as the politicians. Dubai is the go to place.

"Oh! Stop using me as your example," Ko-Ofie remarkeduncomfortably.

"But you are a perfect example""Who said so?"

"I say so!" Anyway, these days, as I said, our local politicians, Imean the "stealers" and pen-armed robbers, have more moneythan people like you.

Ko-Ofie only managed a wry smile.

The homeget snubbed Ko-Ofie's cynical smile and continued, "Anyway, we don't mind how you come by your velvets and the cargo; even if we do, some of us know that

154

you either exaggerate, or don't tell the truth."

"Oh, you do! You think so?"

"Well, the popular assumption is that you guys have to bringthe cargo. And if you fail, especially if the cargo does not contain velvets, the velvet seeker is mocked so you come up with stories to cover up your failures."

Ko-Ofie had wanted to ask the homeget additional questions, but already knew the answers: a velvet seeker who fails to bring home the velvet bankrupts generations of waiters, worshippers,and homegets.

****

There are upper class homegets. They wear wigs and high- heeled shoes. The bigger the wig and the higher the heel, the better recognition one gets in this group. AMBI and OUT OF AFRICA are their ritual ingredients. Ironically, they have neverbeen physically removed from Africa! This group of homegets are also the cheerleaders of corruption in government and business. They serve as signposts to all avenues of corruption.

****

Then, there are the middle class homegets. Members of this group can wait for years before laying eyes on the cargo of returning velvet seekers. They are the patient ones; paradoxically, they cry the most for the cargo. Their cravings for the cargo are unsurpassed. Their minds are constantly focused on these parts. They are the devotees who sing praises all the time about their relatives in these parts. Theirs is a cult. It has a language. They are the perpetual owners of second- hand clothes from these parts. And their second-hand clothes should have numerous tags, pockets, and gadgets embossed with U S of A. Patience in waiting is their virtue. They can wait one thousand years for the return of the velvet seekers. They continue to thrive on the African dream: traveling to these parts is their perpetual objective. The dream occurs one thousand times in their lifetimes. During the waiting period, they keep number plates from Germany, coca cola bottles from the U.S of A. They keep emblems of the Canadian Maple Leaf, the British Union Jack, and vie for the longest Japanese chop sticks. These are not mere souvenirs. They are the essences and relics of the cargo-cult.

****

Another group is known as the lower class homegets. They are equally mesmerized by the antics of returning velvet seekers. They call the velvet seekers the "been-tos." White people are a mystery to them. The lower class homegets are overawed by the velvet, the symbol of the cargo cult. And above all, where the velvet comes from is constructed as a superior world. *Me Buroni*, that is, my white person, is their popular idolizing slogan. The sweetest and the best of everything is prefixed *buroni.* That is the language of their admiration. In short, *me buroni* is a descriptive concept designated for velvet seekers who have supposedly attained the perfection of whites.

****

Ko-Ofie's befuddled thoughts were cut short by a white nurse, who asked, "How're you doing today? You look better than when you were brought in. The doctor will be here very soon to see you. And if you need anything just press the button on the bedpost."

The patient at the far corner coughed and the white nurse went to see to his needs.

Ko-Ofie looked at the nurse for a long time. As his gaze penetrated her lily white skin, he realized that the white skin was not as beautiful as he had thought. There were wrinkles with many tiny grains which appeared to be peeling off.

****

Ko-Ofie thought about AMBI and why it was manufactured in the first place. Then it occurred to him. Brainwashing comes in different forms. In these parts, Africans or blacks, whose mannerisms and lifestyles approximate the white ideal, consider themselves to be more fortunate. Above all, they consider themselves to be better than those who are seen as raw in their embodiment of immemorial Africa. There is also a color complex: a black person with a lighter complexion is seen as more non-threatening than a darker complexioned black person. It is called the CCCNNN Network Syndrome: blacks with lighter skin front for all blacks.

****

"Oh color, color, color..." Ko-Ofie thinly heard his own voice in the distance, but that of the white nurse was more distinct and it had something to do with claiming to be an African-American. Then there was a searing pain in his left arm. He closed his eyes slowly as he experienced hallucinogenic sensation.

****

Ko-Ofie held the sides of his head and a number of unrestrained thoughts raced through his mind. He wished whatever it was that he had said about African-Americans would go away. But it kept coming back. He could not restrain the fact that African-Americans have been made to feel inferior in America. It is the same for the African-British in Britain. And the same goes for African-Canadians. But they look down below the ladder of racism and see continental Africans and Africans from the Caribbean as inferior.

The message carried by institutions of these parts is that diasporic Africans should thank their ancestors and primitive gods for sending them to the cradle of Christian civilization and capitalist slavery. It has been methodically and systemically massaged into the body politic of diasporic Africans that they are better off in these parts. And in this enterprise, acidic racism and crippling discrimination are a part of the package!

In a delirious, dream-like state, Ko-Ofie muttered "Oh, thereis a difference here too. The nearer you are to America like the Caribbean is, the more superior and civilized you are than the unfortunate continental Africans, who are far removed from America."

"What did you say? Are you from America, the United States of America? No you can't be an American! Did you also come over the Trumpian Wall? You're an African, pure and simple.

Please, sleep and don't whisper any of your lies. It may anger other patients," the white nurse remonstrated, as she covered up Ko-Ofie with some blankets.

****

But Ko-Ofie was oblivious of the nurse, except her shadowy, grain-like studded wrinkled skin, which brought back his fading perspectives on the homeget.

****

Taking in a deep breath, Ko-Ofie re-envisioned the homeget. Her face was well-sculpted.

Surprisingly, that was where her beauty ended. A closer look at her face revealed wrinkles and blotches from bleaching, well-hidden under a slab of face powder.

Shifting his gaze from the homeget's face to the far corner of her room, Ko-Ofie saw the final resting place of different types of velvets. Although, he was a matured velvet seeker, he had never seen some of the velvets before. Overall, the velvets were beautiful, especially how they had been carefully manicured and arranged.

****

The painful aspects of the recurring dream returned. The homeget pulled hard at his manhood, and said, "Dr. Kofi Ko- Ofie, hang on, hey give me that stuff. Don't be afraid like all the rest who return. Do you also belong to the dying species?"

The homeget's words struck home to the dismay of Ko-Ofie.

Did he really belong to the dying species?

Thinking about it, Ko-Ofie had asked, "What do you mean by dying species?"

The homeget leaned against the wall and let go Ko-Ofie's flaccid manhood. She stared at the region where his thighs conjoined with his loins for a long time without saying a word.

Ko-Ofie felt very uncomfortable and tried to laugh, but the insides of his mouth cracked. It was as dry as a desert.

"What did you say? What did you say?" These were all that Ko-Ofie could mutter.

Ko-Ofie moved forward and held the homeget's hands, the warmth of which began to revive the deflated ego between his legs.

A vibrant fire lit the homeget's eyes, as Ko-Ofie caressed her fingers. Her breath came in gasps. Ko-Ofie began to explore her warm and supple body.

Finally, Ko-Ofie's finger traveled to the confluence of her thighs, the watershed of life. There, planting the middle finger of his left hand, he squirmed it through the forest of many seasons.

The homeget carefully piloted his middle finger and placed it on a spot. Ko-Ofie knew she was ready for him. As the wetness of the confluence drained around his middle finger, he began to kiss her passionately.

Slowly, Ko-Ofie began to undress the homeget, removing one thing after another. He felt his turgidity gaining a new lease on life. Her body was beautifully carved. He drew back to take a better look. Suddenly, something snapped inside him. The color and texture of her skin looked like a fish that had been roasted alive. Her skin revealed bizarre images of struggle, pain, and anguish.

Very uncomfortably, Ko-Ofie touched the homeget.

The homeget grabbed Ko-Ofie's manhood, looked pleadingly into his eyes, and said, "I've bleached my skin for your return and pleasure, for all of you. Do you understand, not for you alone, but for all of you? Today it is your turn. All for you. Am I white enough now? Am I fair-complexioned enough for you now? Take me and make me whole. Let the final change and the transformation come from you. Take me and make me whole again."

Ko-Ofie grabbed the homeget by her waist. She raised her rightleg to facilitate his entrance.

He crouched over her, but his mind went back to her chapped chameleon-like skin and the assorted velvets and plastic bags atthe far corner of the homeget's room.

As images of bleaching and the velvets besieged his mind, turgidity deserted his manhood again.

Stammering to explain himself, Ko-Ofie rather drew laughter from the homeget.

Laughing intermittently, the homeget said, "Oh, is that all you can do?

Ko-Ofie who was looking at the plastic bags did not say anything.

The homeget stopped laughing, braced herself, and asked, "Why are you concentrating on the velvet? Did your company manufacture the plastic bags too?"

Ko-Ofie thought that the homeget had raised a subject of welcome respite, hence enthusiastically replied, "Oh yes! You know my company even want a female agent to represent our business interest in Ghana, and you are the chosen one."

"Did you say that you want me to be your agent and a representative in Ghana?"

"Yes, you know, you will be a sort of businesswoman-rep," Ko-Ofie intoned.

"Is that the reason why you brought so many of the plastic bagsmanufactured by your company!"

Ko-Ofie quickly surveyed the homeget's room, focused on the plastic bags that he had given to her, and then intoned, "Yes, you know, that is why I brought them. They are samples for whoever wanted to sell them, and be a partner, own shares andso on."

"Does the company belong to you?"

"What would I be doing all these years overseas, in fact, in these parts? Hey, look, we've real property over there."

The homeget got up and moved toward her wardrobe. She pulled out a blouse, waved it around her head as she moved toward the window. She opened the window after fidgeting with its panel.

Rays of light took over the room. Suddenly, the velvet gave off their bright, assailing, and invasive colors.

Ko-Ofie moved closer to the velvets to have a better look. Therewas something else to the velvets: in their new environment, the velvets had become grotesque and bizarre in their beauty.

But there was something strange too: Each velvet had a note attached to it.

Ko-ofie moved closer and stopped short, gasping for breath. His heart-beat increased seconds after reading what the first velvet bore.

Ko-Ofie moved closer again, but was stopped by the homeget, who asked him "What do you want?" "What?"

"What do you want from there? Do you want to take the velvetsand plastic bags back to where you brought them from? Yes, they belong to those who are able to return. I suppose you willgo back very soon. It's an achievement. But you haven't said anything significant about the plastic bags. And I suspect you have little to say about the velvets too."

"Stop, stop it! What are you babbling about?"

"Oh! Dr. Ko-Ofie, you know what I'm talking about. And nothing will stop me from telling you exactly what all of us think about people like you and how your actions have put us into these terrible pull of opposites."

"Well go on. Have your say?"

"Yes, I will. I know you. You think that we should worship you as kings. You see yourself as a king returning after a conquest. You think that you represent warriors returning after the desecration of the enemy. You think that you symbolize fishermen returning from a successful fishing expedition despite a sea storm. But you don't belong to any of these rare achievers!"

"Have you finished?"

"No, I haven't, but who are you to ask me?"

The homeget approached the mirror. Touching her breasts, she held them up as if she was clinically examining them.

Ko-Ofie saw her reflection in the mirror attached to the wardrobe. Once again, he felt a surge in his loins: the bulging nipples looked attractive.

Extending his hands, Ko-Ofie tried to touch the homeget, but she moved away. He saw anger drowning her well-sculptured, but bleached-furrowed face.

As the homeget moved away from him, Ko-Ofie saw the completeness of her bosom.

It was bleached. Then, the surge in his loins became a desire of the past.

"Do I unnerve you?" The homeget asked in a defiant voice. You've the appetite to sleep with me, but you fail to do so because I'm not what you desire. You corrupted our Africaness long ago. You can never understand it. It is too complex for you, more complex than your plastic bags. You are their agents, their messenger, in fact, the carriers of AMBI, OUT OF AFRICA, plastic bags, used toys, and second hand clothes. You don't understand me. Do you?"

The anger in the homeget's mutinous eyes gave way to tears. Ko-Ofie moved closer to comfort the homeget, but she pushed him away, pointed at the velvets, and retorted, "You've taught us all these. You know the implications of all these. I've been around the airport long enough to understand all of you. Your stories about your journeys are so bizarre in the sense that none has spoken the truth about how you acquire the velvets. You wanted to read the various inscriptions on them. Go ahead and read them. You will then understand."

The homeget darted forward as if possessed and tore down the rack that supported the velvets. She stood defiantly on the velvets for sometime, looked at the shock-stricken Ko-Ofie, and began to trample on the velvets.

As tears drowned the homeget's cheeks, Ko-Ofie was overcome with a sudden physical vibrancy. For the first time, he felt like a man. He felt a sudden strength, a surge of energy, even an invigorating enthusiasm. It was a new baptism for him as he witnessed homeget's desecration of so many velvets, the sacred representation of the velvet seekers overseas and their cargo- cult.

Ko-Ofie's thoughts were cut short by the homeget, who had begun to read the bright inscriptions on the velvets:

*MARY AKUA ATOPA:

Place of birth: Ghana.

Residence in these parts: Antwerp, Holland. Educational qualification: B.Sc. Home Science (Ghana).Occupation in these parts: prostitute for Alsatian dogs.Date of departure: 20 May, 1973.

Date of last return: 25 December, 2003. Present condition: barks like a dog.

*JOHNY BRAGGART OWUSU:

Place of birth: Ghana.

Residence in these parts: Las Vegas, U.S. of A.

Educational qualification: M.Sc. Indus. Sc. (Kumasi, Ghana)Occupation in these parts: male prostitute.

Date of departure: 21 June, 1988. Date of last return: 27 April, 2004. Present condition: HIV/AIDS patient.

*MRS JOANNE ONIFIE:

Place of birth: Ghana.

Residence in these parts: London, Britain. Educational qualification: M. Sc. Maths. (Ghana)Occupation in these parts: nanny.

Date of departure: 27 January, 1999. Date of last return: 14 March, 2007. Present condition: insane; sings lullabies.

*DR AMA VIE JOHNSON:
Place of birth: Ghana.
Residence in these parts: Paris, France
Educational qualification: Ph. D. Nursing
Admin. (Europa)Occupation in these parts:
hospital cleaner.
Date of departure: 19 August, 1987. Date
of last return: 29 September, 2015.
Present condition: cancer of the olfactory
organs.

*DR OSQUARE KWARTEN
Place of birth: Ghana
Residence in these parts: Canberra,
Australia. Educational qualification: Ph.D.
Agric. (Ghananianus).Occupation in these
parts: urban elephant hunter.
Date of departure: 1 May, 1980.
Date of last return: 18 December, 2017.
Present condition: hallucinating.

*SAMUEL SAMPSON KO-OFIE:
Place of birth: Ghana
Residence in these parts: Toronto,
Canada. Educational qualification: Ph.D.
Mech. Eng. (Canadus)Occupation in these
parts: potato cutter.
Date of departure: 1 May, 1980.
Date of last return: 18 December, 2021.
Present condition: imbecile and impotent

****

When Ko-Ofie heard his name, shame
over-flooded him.

"Do you know why you went there?" The homeget asked Ko-Ofie just looked on for sometime and stammered, "Why, you know as I do. We all go there for progress," muttered Ko- Ofie.

"You call the acquisition of velvets progress? What about your assorted plastic bags that you accumulated from years of shopping. My God you're the first to espouse this idea that the velvet is a sign of progress. Come to think of it, you've not progressed at all. Decay is written all over you. That's why you always return home to seek rebirth, but you can't be born twice."

The homeget paused to compose herself, collected as many of the velvets as she could, threw them at Ko-Ofie, and carefully mouthed, "Please take them to where they belong. By so doing you may regain your humanity. Your humanity and integrity have been taken away from you. You've nothing to offer except this worthless piece of cloth called velvet. You're like all the rest from Hamburg, Paris, London, and New York. And now you're trekking to places like Tokyo, Alaska, China, Papua New Guinea, Guam, and the Virgin Islands. Ah Dubai is the latest destination."

"Are these the only ones you brought?" The homeget queried, as she eyed the plastic bags.

But Ko-Ofie only cleared his throat.

"Why are you so quiet? Don't you enjoy it here anymore? Hey, man feel at home, keep coming every five years or so and bring your plastic bags. Next time build a factory for plastic bags and stay in these parts forever. Don't you think it's a grand idea?"

The homeget paused as if she was waiting for an answer.

"Hey, why won't you answer my question? I mean the plastic bags! Where were they manufactured? Do they come from many companies? Do you own all of the companies? You must be richer than all the rest that I have ever met. Now, tell me how much do they cost over there? A cent, penny, or are they for free? Do you get them when you shop at grocery stores?

Ko-Ofie didn't answer her. Instead, he took a long breath and gazed at the velvets on the floor.

"Look at you now. You've a very forlorn look. Ghanaian men who have never traveled are not that dead. At least, they talk and laugh. You've a forlorn look in your already tired face. Your smile lingers at the corners of your mouth; they do not brighten your face."

The homeget paused, laughed, and continued, "Your plastic bags have different names. Do they belong to different companies?"

And the homeget coughed, sat on the bed, looked at Ko-Ofie pensively, and continued, "I wish we could talk more. I wish you could be my friend, but you can't. You are like all the rest. You think we homegets should love you because you've just returned from overseas. I would rather like and love the poor and the real African men, those who are not afraid to brave the odds with the hope of effecting change by applying local ideas?"

Ko-Ofie turned around and surveyed all the boxes in the room. They were marked Amsterdam, Berlin, Hamburg, Toronto, New York, Tokyo, Dubai, etc.

Finally, he summoned courage to ask, "Why do you suggest that you like simple things and yet have all these boxes in your room?"

"You don't understand! Do you? What is simple? What is complex? Who decides that? Think about it. You educated fool! These and others, other things, are your wishes, your policies. They are what you teach us, the masses."

Opening his arms, Ko-Ofie sought to embrace homeget to pacify her, but she moved away, and continued, "It's you the policy makers, and all our elites, who whet our appetites for all these foreign and unimportant things."

Ko-Ofie moved back and leaned against the wall.

The homeget looked pensively at Ko-Ofie and continued, "I keep all these boxes with the hope that all of you will return one day, then I can give them back to you. They haven't done me any good. In fact, they don't belong here!"

Clasping his fingers on his ears, Ko-Ofie began to walk away. "Oh, has it come to that. Don't you want to hear me anymore, at least, one more time? You and your kind, the educated elites, the policy makers, in fact, the shit of all of you, have always done things for the masses. At least, I am only speaking my mind; I haven't developed any bastard policy yet. So listen to me, don't walk away."

"Hey say what you want to say. That is it! "Should I continue, Sir Ko-Ofie, Dr. Ko-Ofie?""Stop insulting me."

The homeget paused, pouted her lips, and continued, "You've destroyed me. You may not meet my present state when you return in the future. But you can identify your cargo in thebox that belongs to you. And in that box you can locate whatis destroying me so much. We don't need things which will destroy us in the long run. We need to be who we are. We need to develop our own resources."

Ko-Ofie didn't answer Pointing at her image in the mirror, the homeget asked, "Have you seen my nipples? We have been destroyed long ago. But we keep hoping that one day one of you will make an effort to reject the velvet. But you have only succeeded in turning us intoliving museums of velvets. And I represent many here. Many here, who are increasingly disappointed in you because of yoursuicidal aping of foreign ideas."

"Hey, I think I need to go. You people here imitate the people of these parts more than me! You're making me mad. Takethis complimentary card and when you calm down, you may contact me."

Ko-Ofie fumbled into his breast-pocket, brought out a golden- embroidered complimentary card, and gave it to her.

The homeget read the words carefully, as if any slight mistake would alter the writings on the card.

S. S. Kofi Ko-Ofie, B.Sc., M.Sc., Ph.D.
Consultant, Mechanical Engineer &
Director of White PlasticBags Company.
(Manufacturers of Plastic Bags)
Toronto, Canada.
Phone: office:
GOASSKO0008787881097699999
Cell: GOASSKO000078787190659999

The homeget carefully, but with disinterest, dropped the card as if it was infected with an endemic disease. It was a final celebration for her, and a victorious smile lit her curled lips.

"You have a Ph.D., but it belongs to another land. I have seen many like you. They arrive at the airport often. They have verylittle to say about their culture. So what has your Ph.D. got to dowith Africa? You should have first learnt to improve upon the cast iron our ancestors used before you ride in their cars. And in your case, you should have first learnt to extract para-rubber from the tree of life here before relying on those plastic bags."

The homeget clapped her hands and in a derisive mood said, "Go to hell and burn, for you are of no use to us. You brought different plastic bags that you have accumulated from years of shopping at different places and claimed to be the director of a firm that produced the plastic bags. Don't you know shame?

Ko-Ofie put his hands into his side-pocket and brought out his wallet. Pulling out a wad of fresh US dollars, he thrusted them at the homeget and said, "I'll see you later, you can call me anytime you feel like it. I'm tired of these uncalled for sermons."

The homeget collected the wad of money and spat on it. Then tearing up as many notes as possible, she deposited them on Ko-Ofie's velvet.

Something more painful struck Ko-Ofie. The homeget had been telling the truth, especially her peroration. He looked at her for a long time. He hated her for telling him so much, in reality, truth that called for self-examination.

****

Ko-Ofie felt warm as the white nurse placed a hot towel on his forehead. Then he overheard a faint voice say encouragingly, "Don't say that. You are not going to die. You're too young to die. You'll be okay. Here we don't die young. You know, here we've everything. You won't die; you'll live."

****

Opening his eyes slowly, Ko-Ofie realized he had been dreaming. But as he put the pieces of the dream together, he saw it as a visitation on real life.

****

A sharp pain pierced Ko-Ofie's left thigh. And his eyelids felt heavy. He overheard a faint voice from a distance, mutter, "He would go back to sleep now. No more nightmares."

****

Then the figure clad in white drifted away
and grew fainter and fainter. As the figure
moved away, the message about life and
death became succinct with a twisted
meaning. It was a mutated existence. It was
the death of the living soul. It was unfulfilled
life in these parts.

Chapter Eight

Afua and Ababi sat on a bench near a creek. The park was amply shaded by trees. The sun was at its best. It gave radiance to the summer. Far in the distance, the park merged with a cluster of buildings.

"This is a beautiful park," Ababi remarked.

This was summer; it was the first for Ababi. He surveyed the park with avid interest.

"Yes it's. People come here to do all sorts of things in the summer."

"What do you mean?"

"They come here with their families to play and exercise. Individuals come here to think about their lonely existence. And others come here to read and so on."

Afua had her long legs stretched before her.

Ababi touched Afua's face, and asked, "Do you know that you've two types of complexions?"

Afua looked into the skies as if the answer lurked in the moving clouds.

****

The clouds looked clear and beautiful. Birds chirped in warmth of the sun. But far-off, smog was curling aimlessly.

****

"Yes, I'm aware," Afua finally answered

175

after a long pause.

"Why do you do that to yourself?"

"I told you the other time. I did that for several reasons. ButI'm not about to tell you again. It's personal. And I do regretit! I've come to the conclusion that I need to be happy for me from within. I don't need to be white outside in order to be successful and happy. I've to accept who I am and be happy. I can change the color of my skin and still be alien to the world of these parts. Rather, I should use my beautiful Africaness to change the world."

"I see," Ababi responded, as he turned around and looked far into the distance.

****

The sky was infinitely clear. Small beads of clouds seemed to befighting for space as they formed amorphous shapes.

****

Afua and Ababi overheard a man ask a woman, "Are you having fun?"

The woman looked on unconcernedly and answered, "Yeah, terrific fun, I wish it would be like this always."

"You know," Afua said, "Fun is an individual feeling. It's something one feels within. It's not the superficial outward fun that comes with the individualistic existence in these parts."

Ababi had already noticed that having fun in these part was not a shared feeling.

Pausing for effect, Afua asked, "Now tell me, did you learn about these parts before you left Ghana?"

"Oh, yes, we all did, and I'm sure that those who will come after us will do so too! I did! I left Ghana knowing very well that life and existence in these parts would be better. It is what we've been taught right from nursery to call civilization. But then when you get here, you find out that it's all lies. I think I've to learn to unlearn all those things I was taught about these parts."

"Yeah, you have to. It's the first means of survival here. In fact, you've to shed all those rose colored visions if you wish to understand where you belong here, where you are, and how people and institutions define you."

"I think I know where we are. But as yet I don't know where I belong!"

"I am glad you know where you are. At least, you are not blind yet. When you realize that you need a bulldozer to fight institutionalized racism that's when you will learn where you belong and your political awareness will increase by leaps and bounds."

****

Afua knew Ababi would learn all these things. But it would take time. It would come slowly. He had to shed his rose- colored spectacles. Then, he would begin to understand the haunting beauty of these parts and how its gleam could blind and marginalize the newly-arrived.

****

This is an amusement park where people are supposed to be happy, but they are morbid and sullen! They shelve their despair within. Lonely hearts are slowly torn apart by the snares of this cold, yet combustible environment.

****

"Let us go to that pool. I mean under those trees," Ababi suggested.

One thing surprised Ababi at the pool side. It was the near- nudity and the chivalrous exhibitions of parts of the human body.

Afua noticed Ababi's discomfort and broke the silence, by asking, "Hey, Ababi, do you like all of these naked bodies? Perhaps, you've never seen so many bodies, thinly clad inbikinis of every shape and color, flaunting their naked body parts."

Ababi laughed and said, "Well, I don't know what to say now. But these things are becoming common in Ghana too. Ah! The beaches of Africa where older Western women go after youngerAfrican men. I think they call it sex tourism or so!"

Afua smiled, touched Ababi's lips with her middle finger, and said, "Well, I like your answer. What can you say? Nudity, callit what you want, is accepted here. But they think that as an African you have lived all your miserable existence in your natural nakedness!"

"But this is more ridiculous! How can people of these parts then ridicule the so-called immemorial African nakedness? I mean, after all when a Ghanaian woman breast-feeds her baby in public, it does not have any sexual connotations, not atall."

"Ha, I wish I had seen your nakedness!"

"Oh, what are you saying? Don't corrupt my innocence. I've notbeen here for long," Ababi pleaded.

Afua, ignored Ababi and continued, "Also, they believe that it istoo hot in Africa and that is why Africans go about naked. The other view is that poverty is synonymous with nudity. So that is our naked Mother Africa! But it gets relatively hot here for a few months, yet the worst form of nudity is exhibited!

"Hey you like lecturing. It's something I forgot to tell you," Ababi said amidst laughter.

"Oh stop that and let me finish. I promise you this is my last sermon."

"Is it on the mountain, or on the grass?"

"Let me see, this place is a little hilly, and we are actually on a grassy knoll, well, I guess both."

"Anyway, how many Africans go about naked these days? Let us be a little critical here. And even how many Africans went about naked in the precolonial period? Every society defines nakedness differently. For instance we Ghanaians can breastfeed our babies in public. On the other hand, other societies see thatas a crime, or an aberration of some sort."

"Afua, this is an excellent analysis."

"Thank you, but I'm not done yet! They see pictures of Africanswith prominent nubile breasts. And that is it. They forget that such pictures have religious and aesthetic significance. Many things go unexplained about Africa in these parts. How many Africans dress in skimpy bikinis to parade their behinds at public parks?"

"You're a great teacher! It seems to me, of course, I've not beenin these parts for long, but what they say and think about Africaare the results of their own fears, anxieties, and neuroses."

Afua smiled and bent down to touch some grasses.

"Afua, many foreigners come to Ghana and pleadingly requestfor what I would call touristic cultural pictures for want of a better term. In fact, I didn't know that such photos existed untilI came here. And I didn't know that such photos were broughthere for subtle demonizing."

"So are you saying that all of these are premeditated?"

"I am beginning to see it that way, Afua. Scholars from these parts come to Ghana and arrange, for example, traditionalfestivals to be celebrated to enable them to collect data for their scholarly works. Can you imagine a Ghanaian scholar having the same opportunity?"

"You mean when it is not time to celebrate such festivals?"

"Exactly, that is what I mean. All they have to do is to bribea high ranking official at the Ministry of Culture and Tourism who in turn bribes our indigenous rulers. And, lo and behold, ritual celebrations take place solely for the imperial and neo- capitalist camera lenses as well as hegemonic renderings!"

Clearing her throat, Afua explained, "That's another death, you know, celebrating festivals when they are not due."

"That's very true," Ababi said emphatically, and continued, "My God! I know next to nothing about life here. But Afua believe me, since my arrival here, I've seen the ways that the West using so many avenues distort realities in Africa. And they demean Africans, also known as blacks on TV. In fact, it's a gruesome obsession."

Afua cleared her throat again, and said, "I like your lectures very much. Is this your inaugural lecture?"

"Yes, I wish I had a larger audience. I wish I had the whole world to listen to me, you know. The fact remains that scholars from these parts mockingly explain the purposes and complexities of such festivals to the gullible public of these parts."

"It will continue until every African embarks on a crusade to salvage the name of Mother Africa from the bankrupt Western media and the jaundiced scholarly re/presentations of Africa couched in veiled references to sun, sin, and sex called African Studies."

****

Afua took a few strides, stopped ahead of Ababi, and pointing to a group of women in the distance asked, "Do you like the scenery."

Avoiding Afua's question, Ababi countered, "Is this legal?"

Ababi realized that he had asked a foolish question, laughed uncomfortably, and said, "Why is this not legal with so many people vaunting their bodies? I mean it is the norm right?"

Laughing, Afua touched Ababi's lips with her middle finger, and teased, "Let them hear you ask such questions. They are enjoying the sun's heat. They want a tan."

Ababi replied calmly but very assuredly, "Does it amount to acquiring some blackness?"

Afua shot back, "No white person wants your dark complexion. They merely want a tan, to attain a little ebony. It makes them supple, more beautiful."

"From all the issues you've addressed to me, and the little I've seen, it makes no sense at all. If white is an exclusive and superior color, and black has pejorative connotations, then I don't getit. Why do they tan? Now, Afua, let me honestly ask you this question. Do you respect your color, I mean your blackness, Africaness, or does the color complex go beyond that?"

"Ababi, what is the meaning of respect here. I don't know it myself! Not any more! I've been trying these past twenty yearsto be accepted as one of them. Legalities, statutes of freedom, charters, they don't mean a thing to me!"

"You never answered my question, and neither do I understand you."

"Yes, Ababi, I've told you this before. That is, you lack the experience to understand what I mean. What I want to say is that there are charters, laws, and statutes all stating fairness, equity, and all, but none of them protects me when it comes to covert forms of racism."

"Oh, do you mean to say in effect that policies for the various races are still protected by subtle, systemic laws?"

"Yes, but they are not laws per se; they are warped norms that undermine the laws of fairness."

"Look, Afua, I'm sorry, let us drop this topic, because you are not making any sense."

"What do you mean? Go away and leave me alone," retorted Afua, as she walked away from Ababi.

But Afua stopped abruptly turned around and said, "I know you won't see things my way. It takes time! You've to understand how things are done here. Then the rose-colored spectacles you wear will fall off by themselves. Then, you will see new things about these parts. The danger is that once you shed the rose-colored spectacle, any person in these parts can be an enemy. You will develop instant mechanisms to fight racism, bigotry, humiliation and all that. I assure you that it can be scary sometimes emotionally draining."

"Wow! That is deep!"

"Yes, I think I have reached a point

where nothing makes me more upset than being in the presence of prostituted and spineless scholars like you. The Ghanaian government squeeze huge amount of money from peasants to fund your education! Surprisingly, you and your educated colleagues can't even defend Mother Africa. It is a shame, and shame unto you, young scholar Ababi."

You know Afua, not only that! I'm not surprised! I've met some African students who tried to hide their Africaness in so many ways! Funny, they do such things as if they hate themselves! In Ghana we have some neo-middle classes, mostly educated elites or semi-educated, also called pen-armed robbers, who speak the English Language with their children at home. The children are sheltered from local cultures. Where are our humanity and heritage?"

"What do you mean by humanity? Ababi, don't be too hard on yourself. It's too early for that."

"What I mean by humanity is the self you can identify, that which we can call our own, the historical part of us, but not what someone wants us to become. Look at the vagaries of our bleached skin and our permed hair, or animal weave-on hair! Do they belong to us? They don't belong to anyone either! It is only a cheap imitation of what they want us to be. You may reach whiteness, but can never attain it. Yes, you can never attain whiteness. You feel marginalized, an object of ridicule, when you latch onto other people's way of life. Too many imitations only yield to competitive hatred, Afua! You see what I mean? I'm done. This is my longest speech ever."

"And I guess the most distorted too! Thank you for your telling peroration to my park lectures," Afua remarked laughingly.

"Thank you, chairperson of the park lectures. I shall continue my story by noting that I learnt and read much about the happiness and wealth in these parts from the Afuas whom I met in Ghana before I came here."

"Yes, that's true. I won't challenge you."

"You tell your misadventures in these parts in the first person narrative. I'm now learning that such stories, in spiteof their prose of heroics and victory and mirth, border onunhappiness."

Afua cleared her throat and asked, "What's the significance of the first person narrative?"

"Well you told me and I've added a little to it. Let me remind you again: just keep quiet and listen. The been-tos and the velvetseekers narrate their experiences in the first person narrative. This gives their conceited adventures some false patents of truth, heroism and happiness. In sum, the perceived truth in the misguided stories about these parts makes their audiences in Ghana welcome the heroic narrators and epic story-tellers with pomp and pageantry."

"Your analogy is getting deeper than mine."

"Ignoring Afua's comment, Ababi continued, "The narrative pattern and the welcome ceremonies have their own rituals. Such rituals enable as many velvet seekers as possible to qualify as priests of the faith of cargo-cult."

Afua broke into a hysterical laughter. But Ababi was quiet and pensive, even when she poked his rib-side. Ababi pulled away gently and said, "I never finished what I was saying. Let me continue."

"Really, you didn't finish it?" Yes, let me finish," pleaded Ababi seriously, "One must also have gone through the process of skin peeling and chemicalized haircoloring, or the wearing of horse hair. If they are rich enough, surgery is the answer to having aquiline noses and thin lips to boot."

Afua responded angrily, "Look, I did not bring you here to insult me."

"Oh! Sorry oh! This is not an insult. And I was not even referring to you. Afua, I am only restating what diminishes our dignity and heritage as Africans, whether continental or diasporic. And we must face it now or never. It goes deeper than that. We must be proud of who we are first before everything else."

Ababi was so engrossed in his point of view that he did not see Afua sob.

****

Afua was reminded of the velvets and all the humiliations associated with them. She knew that all velvet seekers had failed the young SEKODOMES: the unborn and the living dead. Why the people of Ghana think that these parts are an unsurpassed paradise was still not clear to her. She had laboredat understanding for far too long.

****

Ababi took her hand and said, "I didn't mean to upset you. I was also carried away. I'm sorry."

****

Ababi felt extremely sorry for making Afua upset. In order to change the subject, he pointed to a man and girl, and asked, "Are they lovers?"

Afua stopped sobbing and asked, "Who are you referring to?"

"Oh that pair holding hands! Look, he is touching her waist. Oh! He is touching her breasts in a funny way."

"I am sure they are a father and a daughter. The girl is just abouttwelve or thirteen years old."

"Why should her father keep touching that part of her body?

Strange things happen in this civilized public park."

"Oh! Ababi, stop it. It is affection. That is the way it is. Anyway,we don't want to be too critical. Cultures differ. We know that."

As father and daughter held hands, they navigated toward a parking lot.

Ababi touched Afua's shoulder and remarked, "Wow, talk about real cultural shock!"

"Did you see that? Look, the father is

kissing her!""Oh, stop it!"

"Afua, this is a wonderful world! I never read about it in their scholarly journals. Neither did I see it in Hollywood movies, newspapers, magazines, and all the stuff we hear and see in Africa about these parts. So why is it that none of you has told us about such bad and sickening happenings?"

****

The guilt showed on Afua's face. But she remained calm. She tried, in fact, she had tried to recount her experiences, indeed, the African epic, but it was to no avail. Whatever be the case, any message of doom is bound to carry its own confusions, its own tragedies, and its own pitfalls. Afua didn't want to be the bearer of a message of doom that would be wrongly perceived by the waiters. Besides, Afua was aware that many devotees of the velvet in Africa hallucinate about California's beaches, the Union Jack, the London Bridge, New York's Empire State, the Niagara Falls, Abraham Lincoln's freedoms, the American CivilWar, and above all the American dream and its slang. Who would listen anyway? The TV, the satellite dish, and the glossy magazines embossed with nude white females, make life seem rosy in these parts. Of course New York, Washington DC, Paris,and Toronto are attractions themselves. These days Africans talk about Dubai! And lately, there are African-American magazines, which are also obsessed with white-looking black women! All these and others act as strong counter narratives themselves that undermine the meta-narratives of velvet seekers who are bold enough to tell the truth about these parts.

****

"Afua are you here with me?"

"Yes, where else do you think I'm?""But I asked you a good question!"

"I know, Ababi, but I can't provide any answers. What would have happened if someone had told you all about the terrible things in these parts? Wouldn't you have concluded that that person didn't want you to be a part of the great circular flows of history between Africa and the rest of the Atlantic World?"

"No, I wouldn't have said that. Rather, I would have appreciated that very much. Indeed, many of us would like some of you to be honest with us. That way, we the youth, the vibrant ones, not the aged who have wasted their time on dreaming about these parts, would stay at home and develop Africa."

"You think so?"

Looking at Afua with the posture of someone who was sure of himself, Ababi replied, "Yes, I believe so. African high school and university students think about nothing, but how to travelto these parts. Afua, believe me, it's a very dangerous obsession.It's a fixation that is destroying the cultural fabric of African states and societies."

Remembering SEKODOME and

EMPIRE STATE and all that, Afua asked, "Is it that bad?"

"Yes it's that bad, Afua. I think the average Ghanaian thinks that to be successful in this life, he or she has to travel to these parts."

"Why, what reason are there to give?"

"Afua, just imagine that you leave Ghana penniless. Within a few years you return to Ghana and you are seen as a cedi-millionaire!"

Ababi paused for effect and continued, "Yes, you are a millionaire overnight. There are other benefits such as healthcare, environmental cleanliness, adequate food sources. Our leaders can't invest in good healthcare facilities, but go overseas to seek better healthcare."

"Oh! I am aware of that."

"Okay, as I was saying, once been-tos return from these parts, they bring home unsurpassed riches, and believe me, overnight, they command every respect available."

Hoping to egg on Ababi, Afua retorted, "Is it really true?"

"It's incredible how these been-tos are worshipped by their fellow Ghanaians! This speaks to the moral bankruptcy of the whole society. You know, once you go home with the US dollars, also known as "In God We Trust;" the British pounds; the Japanese yen; and the Euro; in fact, you can prolong your life if you want to. You are worshiped at the altar of superiority. And if you can slang, it is an added advantage. It is as simple as that. But things are changing"

"Keep on brother," Afua stated.

Ababi resumed, "There are exceptionally rich people in Ghana than Ghanaians who live in these parts. How they make their wealth I can't explain. But those in the public and civil services, parodied as "stealers," are something else. Some are paid about 400 dollars per month, but have palatial mansions, a fleet of expensive cars, and educate their kids overseas. They are magicians, or what else!"

Afua somewhat surprised said, "Eh! Is that so?"

Ababi continued, "But we've not answered one particular question yet! Guess what! And it's how the been-tos or returnees get the wealth and riches they bring to Ghana? It's important to me because it seems to me that Africans in these parts are marginalized, living on the periphery of society. Of course, a few are relatively better off, especially the well-educated, who hold good-paying jobs."

Touching Ababi's shoulder, Afua asked, "My gentleman, what're you driving at? That I am poor?"

"Oh no! Yet a big question, I guess. It seems to me that irrespective of the jobs that Africans do in these parts, they're still the dogs of society. I think that we need to stay at home to develop our own economies."

Afua replied, "What about the oppressive governments that deter citizens from helping in nation-building? And too much envy, entitlement mentality, and crabs-in-a- bucket mentality, indeed, the so-called pull him/her down syndrome!"

"Oh, Afua, does it mean that all citizens living under oppressive regimes must desert their countries? Then what becomes of their countries? The African masses must stay and fight the educated "stealers" and pen-armed robbers."

Ababi smiled and surged ahead of Afua.

"And what answers do you have?"

Walking backwards with arms stretched, Ababi responded, "I believe that the visceral attachment to one's nation is much more important than the addictive material things acquired overseas. And we should know that dictators, oppressors, name them, do not get up one morning and announce democratic or human rights reforms. The African masses have to fight for reforms and change."

"Hey, I've never seen you like this before," Afua interjected as she jumped playfully to catch up with Ababi.

"Please let me finish my point," Ababi remarked as he gently swung aside to avoid Afua, "Until, we decide to fight for such rights, until we opt for a cultural revolution, and until such cultural revolutions are successful, the Bank of the World can give us all its monies, stocks, bonds, and so on, but the system will fail in Africa.

"So what do you mean by a cultural revolution in this context?" Taking in a deep breath, Ababi replied, "Something that will generate public awareness that the state is no one's property. And that those in responsible positions don't have the right to abuse their power, misuse the national wealth, and so on."

"Wow! What a revolutionary," Afua interjected.

"Yes, we need to bring to an end the materialism that is eroding the moral basis of the state."

Ababi put his arm around Afua and said, "Let us go there," and pointed to an area of the park shaded by tall buildings.

The tall buildings entombed the park and looked desolately into the sky. Their glass-ornamented walls and somber lights from within made them appear like exhumed caskets placed against a wall. Eclipsing the battered beauty was an eerie silence that forced the mind to think about life and death.

As they walked toward the end of the park, Ababi declared, "Afua this park, like most places in these parts, has an artificial beauty that is exhilarating, but also somber."

"Yes, I agree. There is a ring of emptiness to it. It is an environmental conquest that has ended in social ruins."

****

Only the innocent children seemed to understand and have a grasp of the air of stifled happiness that ruled the park. They ran after nothingness, but appear to understand its message. Their parents appeared numbed. Each parent and child did their own thing, took their own strides, and hardly bothered to realize the physical presence of others. Parents moved with their children on intrinsically allotted spots.

193

****

Afua and Ababi passed by some elderly people, whose buttocks were glued to defined spots, and whose forlorn eyeballs seemed to focus on nothingness in space. And whose ears were antennas to an unfathomable present and an unknown future.

Afua pointed at an imposing white building that shadowed the park and said, "I am sure most of the old people you see here live there."

"Do they live there with their families? I mean do they have an apartment like yours?"

"No, it is a special home for old people. They call it old people's home."

"You mean they house old people in special homes!"

"Stop acting surprised," Afua shot back.

"Who told you that you I'm acting?"

"But you don't believe it. That's the way of their world."

Ababi laughed and said, "Yes, I think it is the way of their world."

Laughing, Ababi asked, "So where are their families? Why is it that they are not living with them? I can't believe that old people are treated this way."

"Well, in these parts, they don't see it that way. In Ghana, the older you are the more respect you gain. Also, in Ghana, the elderly are accorded respect and occupy special place within the social structure. Here, in these parts, they just exist. They're just one of the worn out disposable cogs in the wheels of life in these parts and their so-called civilization."

"But Afua, things are changing in Ghana now. If you don't have dollars, pounds, Euros, and what have you, whether you are old or young, you've no enviable place in any social structure."

Ababi jumped in front of Afua and pleadingly requested, "Afua, let me present my last lecture now."

"Well, what shall we call this one? Ababi Memorial Lectures?

Go ahead. I won't stop you; I am listening."

"Okay, okay, right from nursery, mention them, the university, movies, books, name them, I was made to understand that these parts are a paradise of civilization. But I see strange and odd things anywhere I go. This is their world where beer drinking is ritually-advertised with women's breast and legs. All the incests, murders, homelessness, serial killings, and massive gun-related deaths. They have all the violent crimes in the world. Mother Africa you can rest."

"Well, you seem to gradually understand these parts! Good for you.

"Thank you, chairwoman, or rather chairperson, of the park lecture series, I'm done."

Afua broke into a hysterical laughter and gently nudged Ababi in the midrib.

Two white children ran in front of them; Ababi pointed at them and said, "Hey Afua, so these young ones will one day be sent to the old people's home!"

"Yes, that's their life-style, you don't seem to understand what development and civilization of these parts can do to a people."

"Do the old people get what they need to survive?"

"Yes, they are provided with everything they need to make life livable and pleasant."

"Exactly what do you mean? You've said that you've everything, yet you're not happy. Are they happy in their circumstances since they also have everything?"

"No Ababi, material things do not always make life a happy one. One needs recognition and acceptance as a human being. That's what I lack here. I've lived long on the periphery of the culture of these parts. Sometimes, I feel I could get lost and nobody would bother to look for me."

"This must be a strange world!"

"Not only that. It's an artificial world."

"You know, I see smiles dancing at the corners of white people's mouth anytime I meet them. And these are people I don't know. Is it a part of the artificial world?

"Yes, but it includes guilt too."

"Afua, you're more than a teacher, and you will continue to bea special person in my life, but I want to look at life in these parts from my own perspectives based on my own lived-experiences."

Laughing, Afua replied, "Yes, Ababi, you're right. For a long time, my perspectives have been battered by the system in these parts. Hence my lectures may be lopsided and biased!"

"Afua, I didn't mean it that way. What I meant was that many things here puzzle me, and I will rather learn from experience.

Simply, I've come a long way, but I'm sorry, I still don't seem tounderstand many things in these parts."

Afua looked up and said, "I thought we agreed the lectures were over. The best thing for you will be to experience what lifehas in store for you in these parts."

"You've a beautiful soul, Afua. And, I wonder why with all thatyou are not happy in these parts."

They got up and walked on. Ababi tried to trace the outline of his shadow, but it proved elusive; it moved when he moved.

"Ababi, why are so quiet? Are you also unhappy?"

"No, I'm not, but I was wondering about what you meant by living on the periphery of the mainstream culture."

"I don't want to burden you with my felt-needs. I need people to recognize me as a human being, but not by the color of my skin. Not my color, your color too," Afua stopped and touchedAbabi's forehead.

"I've been to places in these parts. A look, a glance at my color reveals all my credentials and credibility in negative ways. All my tastes are known by the shape of my mouth and nose. Conclusions have been made by reducing everything to my mere skin color, the thickness of my lips, and the broadness of my nose. My skin is a text. Any idiot can read it. And sometimes, you know what, I've wept inside. Yes, while working with them, eating, and laughing with them, I'm considered their dog. It's that they love dogs, have national associations for dogs, find them nice places to sleep, even hospitals, but dogs are never their co-equals. You're also a dog. Ababi we are dogs in their collective estimation."

"Hey no long lectures! And they have dog welfare associationsand all that? But you said there are homeless people! Is that not a paradox?"

"There are many things in these parts that are shelved from Africans in Africa. May be that's what makes us come on modernjets, the new slave ships. Even crossing the S We are enticed with the toffees and the statues of liberties of the Atlantic. It is only when you get here that you realize that there are no toffeesor freedoms at all. Rather, a cocktail of imperial and racist bile of discrimination rule these parts.

Ababi looked at Afua`s tear-bathed face and comfortingly said, "I can't understand it. Are you that unhappy out here?"

"You will only understand when you come to learn the meaningof all those prostheses they wear, their vaunted decorum, and all their artificial smiles."

Ababi edged closer to Afua and whispered, "Afua there is wisdom in your words. We are outsiders, but those within, those who are in the mainstream of these parts, are blind sufferers. Let us move to the other end, it's getting too sunny here."

"No let us go home now. I'm tired. I can use some rest."

Afua took Ababi's hand and placed it around her mid-section. There, in the artificially-sculptured world, an inscription

met their gaze: it read THE WHITE
WORLD OF LIEIUTENANT-
GOVERNOR'S PARK.

Only the two of them had been there,
black of course. But all around them,
someone was lurking, watching, and prying.
Anda thousand eyes bore into every step they
took.

"I will learn too. I will learn more about
THE WHITE WORLD OF
LIEIUTENANT-GOVERNOR'S PARK
OF THESE PARTS," Ababi whispered.

Chapter Nine

Peering through the windows of his tenth-floor apartment, Ababi saw the much anticipated snow.

The trees stood still, angry at the departure of the summer's bloom and zest. Only the needle pines flaunted their wintry leaves to the world.

Ababi stood in the lobby of his apartment building. Stretching ahead of him was a ghastly mass of snow. The streets were empty except for a few homeless people who were glued to well-defined spots. It was too cold for a merry Christmas morning. The homeless people had their hands in their pockets, giving their shoulders stiff postures as in death.

****

Ababi had asked his white classmates about the relevance of white Christmas. No one had offered an answer. He did not press any further. He understood it now. It was that simple.

****

Ababi's thought was broken by the sound of a car horn. It was Afua's.

Afua stretched to open the car door for him. Rubbing her hands, Afua smiled and said, "Happy Christmas. Did I keep you waiting?"

"No, I just came down; happy Christmas," Ababi replied, as he sat in the car, and remarked, "The streets are empty!"

"I know. This is the period when people remain indoors, shut off from the rest of the world. It's the period of mean coldness, yet the period of hope, renewal, and rebirth."

"I see."

"Ah! It's hope and renewal found in treasure and Christmas boxes placed under Christmas trees."

****

This was Ababi's first Christmas in these parts. Back home, Christmas was simple. There was no black or white Christmas. It was simply Christmas. He remembered its simplicity, its camaraderie, and how it bonded communities and families together.

****

"What are you thinking about?"

Ababi cleared his throat and said, "The simplicity of Christmas back home."

Surprised, Afua said, "Christmas back home is not simple. Not at all! It involves another journey to the dominion of the velvets in these parts. It's the season that introduces the velvets. The cargo may be made up of simple things, but they are insatiable and addictive. And you know that the celebration of Christmas is always cyclical."

Ababi asked, "Why is it cyclical?"

"Simply put, the devotees of the cargo will always go for it, irrespective of the tortuous nature of the journey. In fact, when one cycle ends another begins! And here we are on a wintry journey to celebrate our loneliness during Christmas."

"Yes this is winter, the winter of my Geography lessons in Ghana. Afua you seem to be your own critic!"

"All I know is that such are life's lessons based on lived- experiences shaped by the forces of change and dehumanization. I understand it all, but breaking free is not easy."

Ababi surveyed the vast expanse of snow lying undeterred ahead of them and cheerfully replied," But at least, I've one thing going for me. Now I'm on the pathway of self-discovery that comes from without and self-empowerment that comes from within. These are important. Paradoxes!"

"That's good to hear," Afua replied.

****

Huge unorganized monuments of snow covered the land. The stretch of land ahead of them possessed a disturbing peace of its own. It was like an uninhabited land dotted with deserted homes. The land was barren of any human sound. Occasionally, souls in drowning winter accoutrement appeared in sight. And they looked as dead as the soundless stretch of the snow-clad landscape.

****

Ababi found a certain urge to rise above the overpowering Christmas loneliness. But the cold numbed his sense of anticipated enjoyment. Anyway, it was the same during the summer. There was happiness, but in a solitary manner.

Individuals hugged their allotted plots of happiness. It dawned on him that he had to hunt for happiness in these parts. After all, he had read so much about happiness in these parts from textbooks, magazines, newspapers telegrams, etc.

****

Seeking answers to his thoughts, Ababi asked, "Afua, so is this what Christmas here is all about? From what I heard from some of you, it's so glamorous!"

"Well, we've not been able to tell the truth to those back home in Ghana. It's because we lost parts of our heritage long ago. Such parts are irretrievable, lost in foreign lands forever."

"Yes, within that loss, our Africaness and Africa loom large, emerging as a dismal shadow."

Eh! Ababi, you are no longer an outsider. Now, you're a true insider. No, better still, you are a true Africanist Philosopher."

"Africanist, that is too familiar," Ababi laughed.

"Why?"

"I remember a lecture given by Professor Redd Racy Naked, a renowned Africanist. The title of his paper was:

"NINETEENTH-CENTURY AFRICANISTS & TWENTIETH CENTURY AFRICANISMS"

"What is it about Africanists?"

"Actually, I don't remember Prof Naked's definition. It's rather the reaction of the elite Ghanaian audience that I vividly remember."

"But you are a member of that elite, so why don't you refer to them as my colleagues, the elite Ghanaian audience? After all, you give audience to anyone who speaks through the nose," Afua teased, as she laughed.

"Oh stop that," Ababi replied reflectively, and continued, "Are you listening?"

"Yes, my elite lord," Afua teasingly responded, "Please, we're waiting for your lectures."

"Okay the audience was largely made up of Ghanaian scholars with doctoral degrees. They basked in the fact that they had been educated overseas. And they belonged to various schools of thought and ideologies.

"You mean your audience. Just joking and pulling your legs!

Which schools of thought anyway?"

"Oh, they included the Revisionist Apologists, Socialist Clubs, the Victorians or the Englandists, the Bourbons or Frenchists, the Romanovs or Russianists, and the Lincolnites or the Americanists. Ha, sometimes, the Americanists call themselves the Statue of Libertarians! Of course, we have the Asianists! Anyway, they were all baking in borrowed imperial gowns of their respective former schools."

Ababi stopped laughing and in a more serious tone, continued, "The mentors of the Ghanaian elite were also present."

"Who are those role models or mentors?"

"Nineteen and twenty-year olds from these parts, mostly university, trade school, and high school graduates, at best with bachelor degrees to match their white pedigree."

"And how do they get to go to Ghana to become role models?"

"They are mostly on the tickets of the IMF, BTA, CIDA, OXFAM, AFS, CUSO, Peace Corps, etc. You know, some go to Africa for the mere sake of imperial adventurism."

"I see, but you should add PCP, DDT, and HOLLYWUUD STARDOM!"

Ababi paused, laughed, and continued, "I am going to say something very good on their behalf! The logic of their going to Africa is that havens of poverty abound there. And it's believed that white graduates who can't make it in their own country can turn things around in Africa."

"Oh, stop joking. What was the conclusion of the white professor?"

"He said that Africans were still living in the nineteenth century and would continue to need the help of "First Utmost World".

In a more serious tone, Ababi continued, "According to him, the First Utmost World was his new name for the group of richest nations in the world and they exclude any African nation."

"Rich in what terms? And did he add that the so-called "First Utmost Nations" are the most morally bankrupt in the world?"

"Oh, let me continue; it's a long story, you know."

"Go on! Make it juicy."

"Okay, Professor Naked's conclusion was apparently well- received. In fact, the Ghanaian chairperson for the occasion, who was wearing three academic gowns, continued to clap even when Professor Naked boldly asked him to stop clapping.

"Three academic gowns, you mean! What is the significance of those three gowns?"

"Oh, so you don't know! They symbolize first degree, second degree, and a third degree. Oh, the chairperson had a fourth gown. This one was resplendently displayed at the back of his chair. And the front pocket carried a bold inscription that had the ultimate message of a recently awarded honorary doctorate degree by the University of Europa-Americus.

Afua laughed.

Ababi stopped talking, as an elderly white man suddenly appeared in the horizon of the snow-clapped landscape.

The elderly white man was wearing a green coat that looked like a parachute and a red hat that did not adequately cover his ears. There were snowflakes on his ears. Occasionally, he tilted his head sideways to shake the snow off his ears.

The elderly white man pulled out his hands from his coat pocket, slammed his left hand on his ears, and as a result lost balance and fell in the snow.

Afua exclaimed, "Sorry," and mockingly

asked, "Sir, is there any black ice out there? White people don't do well on black ice!"

"Oh, Afua, be kind to the gentleman on black ice."

Afua stopped the car and Ababi stretched his neck to look at the elderly white man, and then rushed out of the car to help him.

The elderly white man's thundering fall had removed the snow on his ears, and his reddened ears looked like an umbrella with its inner springs broken.

Ababi pulled up the elderly white man, beamed a smile, and said, "Merry Christmas."

The elderly white man looked at Ababi with a sheepish grin and responded, "There is no Christmas, at least not for me. I'm just moving on, searching, and celebrating a lost life!"

"Oh! I'm very sorry."

"Look, you better go on your journey. There is no life or happiness here or there, not that I know of," the elderly white man intoned, as he looked at the direction, where Ababi and Afua were headed.

Shivering from the cold, Ababi left the elderly white man. "Hmm! Did I do the right thing? I mean helping that man!" Afua replied, "There is a story about a black man with anemic locks of permed blonde hair. Our black hero had tried to help a white lady who had sustained an injury from a fall. It happened that our illustrious black man was the only non-white nearby when the accident occurred. And he was the only one who offered to help. Another surprise! Our illustrious black man was charged for indecent touching."

"This is an interesting story of criminalized black deliverance.

Hmm! You can be philosophical sometimes!"

****

Afua's message struck Ababi. Learning about these parts came in degrees, by leaps and bounds. But it's the understanding that matters in the long-term.

"You know since I've been here, many incidents have pried into and assaulted my very being, my very humanity. Is it because I'm an African?"

"Oh, people ask questions out of ignorance," Afua quipped and laughed, then assuming a serious posture and tone, continued, "But such incidents and prying questions don't stem from curiosity nor ignorance. They come from perennially cultivated and carefully nurtured racial bigotry."

****

Thinking about the elderly white man, Ababi intoned, "But that man was kind to me: he did not press any charges against me."

"Well, well, he will come after you tomorrow!"

Ababi smiled and asked, "Afua, did you see what the man was wearing. His dress suits his environment, I mean the weather. We

Africans wear woolen suits even when the temperature is very high."

"Don't tell me that you're becoming critically obsessed with your own people, the educated elite. You see they are the collaborators."

"Yes, they are!"

"You collaborate with the people of these parts. You have accepted their institutions and norms without one damn question asked. Besides, a few years ago, you were governing from the ancient slave castle. And you had adorned the castle with imported flowers from Sweden, Holland, Spain, Portugal, France, and Britain. These were the suppliers of flowers that enchanted you, the elite inhabitants of the slave castle, which was the seat of postcolonial governments in Ghana."

"Afua is something wrong with us? Why are all these thoughts creeping through our minds on this deserted road when we should be anticipating Father Christmas?"

****

But, Afua offered no answer. There was an apparent pain in her face.

****

Ababi had come to understand what Afua's pain was all about. Recently, he had also been saturated with so many deep lacerating thoughts. Such thoughts came with parallels to be made and conclusions about things he had not experienced. But now he understood scenes that initially lacked meanings at both ports of departure and entry.

****

Ababi remembered his departure, the airport, and all the warmbye-byes that came from so many well-wishers. There wereso many people who were just happy for him because he was leaving for the proverbial greener pastures.

Then it occurred to Ababi that Africans had been fooled the second time around. The first time was when the European colonized the continent. The second time around is Africans are allowing themselves to be colonized in these parts.

****

Ababi could not bring himself to think things through and hence broke the ensuing silence by saying, "Afua what do you think about the processes that bring us here?"

"I think it's a complex one, but there are some aspects that are fascinating."

"And what are those fascinating aspects?"

"Oh, as Ko-Ofie always explains what brings us to these parts involves rituals of departure performed by the worshipers, the waiters, the homegets, the dreamers, and all those who hope tobe velvet seekers in the future."

"Ababi, you're a good student!"

"And you're a great teacher. Afua what

was your departure like? I mean when you were leaving Ghana?" "You don't want to hear it all over again! Do you?"

"Well, I've been thinking about all the rituals that informed my departure."

"Actual rituals, you mean?"

"The departure is an inexorable process that links velvet seekers to these parts. There were unexpected embraces from people I didn't know. How does that sound? There were also instant smiles of congratulations from many people. Everyone, it seemed, was happy for me. It's a complete public celebration."

"Ababi, mine was the same. Why is it a public celebration?"

Ababi replied, "Oh, people think that one is lucky when they get to leave Ghana, sort of leaving behind the pain of living. But, now how I wish they could be in these parts to see our alienation and rustic life!"

"Coming here has been the worst pain in my life. The worst form of self-bondage," Afua sadly intoned.

"Yes, I can understand."

Recollecting the happy faces of the devotees, waiters, and worshipers behind the massive glass-shield curtains of the airport, Ababi continued, "Afua do they go to the airport to inspire those traveling to these parts."

"It's not as simple as that. But yes, they inspire us and they make us feel that we've achieved it all. But it's also their dream that one day they will also depart. They also hope that the departees will bring the velvet to be shared among them.

"Oh, now, I understand!"

Afua giggled and continued in a tone of mockery, "But the inspiration comes from a departee's speech, gait, assorted bleached complexions, and weird hairdos and so on. But it also depends on whether it's the departee's first or second travel to these parts! Have I made my point?"

****

Suddenly, the car jerked, and Afua said, "Oh, my God, that's black ice."

"You said something about black ice when the elderly white man fell down! What is black ice anyway? I asked my classmates about it, but none was willing to offer any answer."

"Oh, black ice! That's when the roads become very slippery due to the accumulation of solid flattened ice" "Black, black, and black, and it imputes negativity to everything." Afua stopped talking. And Ababi also remained quiet.

Ababi felt in unison with the deceptive movement of the car's shadow on the glittering snow. As unreal as it seemed, the sun's ray on the snow dazzled him.

****

And Ababi felt entombed by a momentary peace. It came with something he had desired long ago. It was mesmerizing. It was the dream of living in these parts. This was the world he had heard so much about from the velvet seekers, the velvet worshippers, the waiters, the homegets, and the dreamers of thedream. This was the world he had seen in movies, magazines, newspapers, on TV. Now, he was living the reality of the dream.And it was an ordeal.

****

The weather became colder. Ababi tried to blow his nose, but he could not. The gloves protecting his hands from the cold- numbing effects of winter hindered his efforts. He removed the glove on his left hand and performed the ritual of de-icing the nostrils. Then, he brushed his right palm over his eyes, for theywere hurting from the chilling effects of the cold weather.

****

"What are you looking at? And why are you so quiet this Christmas morning?" Afua asked as she shifted a little in the driver's seat.

Ababi touched Afua's shoulders and said, "Shh! But I thought we didn't have to chat so that you could outwit the black ice. Anyway, I was just looking at the wooden electric poles or utility poles as you call them here."

"What about them?"

"Oh, the wood, it is a great contrast. Back home they use cementpoles.

****

Adjusting his seat belt, Ababi repositioned

his head, and folded his arms across his chest. He began to reflect on an IMF-sponsored electrification project in his own locality, an area with a population of about thirty thousand. Cement poles werepreferred to wooden ones. Faced with a shortage of five cementpoles, the project was abandoned. But hard wood trees, the typeGhana exported to these parts, were abundant in the area. No doubt such trees could have been used, instead of the cement poles.

****

Ababi knew that something had stirred in him. And he knew he was coming to it, emerging from it all with a novel awareness and self-empowerment.

****

Sitting up, Ababi looked straight ahead. The mass of white desert stretched farther into the distance. His thoughts mergedwith the vast expanse of impenetrable snow. The trees that lined the avenue appeared sullen and mournful against the moody background of the vast desert of snow. It was a horizon that revealed nothing except a disturbing, hollow emptiness. Crouching hills emerged at places where they were not visible in the summer months. The trees that caressed the landscape now stood bereft and forlorn. The church at the junction of the crouching hills stood alone, with its steeple looking into the empty heavens.

****

Ababi turned his gaze away from the church building, touched Afua's hand, and asked, "May we talk now?"

"Yes, you may."

"Do you think I'm still an outsider?"

"Oh, well, you may not be an outsider as such, but you're still on the periphery, and you belong to the marginalized minority."

"I see now! I have come a long way. Now I understand so many things about these parts. Marginalized minority also known as visible minorities?"

"Well, the pressures, the uncertainties, and all that are brought to bear upon us, force us to assess our experiences in these parts. It's a just reaction to an unjust action."

****

But, Ababi had heard that outsiders, sometimes with detachment and the bearings of the innocence of children, as well as with cultural relativity of strangers, are better able to learn more about their host societies than what insiders are capable of coming to terms with.

****

Despite, the presence of Afua, Ababi felt alone and deserted in the streets of his first ever Christmas in these parts. Afua had built a dam of happiness for him. She had invited him to a Christmas party, which was going to be attended by Africans.

Afua made a turn, driving as carefully as she could on the snow.

The snow looked very fresh and pristine, and Ababi couldn't help it, but remembered the popular nursery rhyme. He smiled and said aloud "As white as snow."

Smiling back. Afua intoned, "As white as snow, beautiful, pure and pristine snow. Black ice and all that! Okay we're now at home."

Afua locked the car doors, and said, "Well, they say the early bird catches the worm."

As they approached Afua's apartment, a suffusion of a dirge boomed through the corridor.

Ababi clasped his fingers, and asked, "Who is playing this liturgical dirge at this Christmas hour?"

As they ploughed through the corridor, variations of the dirge emerged from the apartments on Afua's floor.

Ababi took Afua's hand and pleaded, "Let us hurry away from here."

"No, we can't. We are part of it already. We are here. And the dirge is for all of us, the living dead. This is the corridor of the living dead. It is for us too."

"But, you said that we are outsiders and that we are marginalized.

How come we are a part of this corridor?"

"We are all the more marginalized, because the insiders have refused to recognize what this outsider status is doing to us. No one sees you in this corridor. That is the outsider status and marginalization. Their inaction is our continued isolation, pain and decay in this corridor. And our actions are seen as signals of the unassimilated other"

"Is this deliberate?"

"Yes, it's. Yes, it's the fear that if they let us in, we will know their masked sufferings in their shitholes and strife for an Africa whose developments and images we can call our own, our own positive creation."

"So what you are saying is that we are outside, but are trying to examine an entity we don't understand."

"I think so, but it's more complex than that. It's not that we don't understand. We do so as outsiders whose voices have been marginalized."

"Do you hear it? The dirge is becoming louder and louder as we approach your apartment."

Afua did not respond, but hurriedly knocked at her door. "Hi, come on in," someone responded.

Afua remarked, "Oh, did I wake you up?

Afua took the man's hand, pointed at Ababi to the man, and said "This is our second guests. He is called Ababi!"

The man tapped on Ababi's shoulders, and said, "I am, eehh, Moses, Thanks be to God and may God bless you this Christmas morning. Thank you Lord."

There was something awkward, something cosmetic about Moses that was repugnant. But it didn't surprise Ababi anymore. Many Africans he had met in these parts flaunted the same borrowed European mannerisms with pride.

Moses gazed at Ababi's hair, smiled, and uttered, "Very new in the promised land, I suppose."

Afua came back from the kitchen and offered a bottle of beer to Ababi.

Moses continued to look at Ababi's hair.

No one spoke, but the silence was suddenly broken by Moses, who declared, "May we pray for the restoration of our souls," as he brought out a prayer book from his breast pocket.

"I am reading from the prayer book of Black Church on White Earth. The reading is taken from part three: Messages for the Newly Arrived. Let us pray. Oh God, we thank you for making it possible for one of us to also sojourn in these parts. Let him fully assimilate the life in these parts, the life to be led in the next century and beyond."

As Moses prayed, a shadow of gloom shaded the corners of his eyes. His voice rose and gained an ear-tearing tone. And a confluence of foam formed at the corners of his rapidly twitching mouth and drained the furrowed valleys in his chin area.

Moses wiped away the foam, and continued, "And bless us in our learning so that we will be able to throw away our past, including language, history, culture, and all others. Help us to change our names to suit the ears of our venerable hosts. Oh Lord, teach us to go through all our sufferings in these parts so that whatever we learn here can be emulated by those in Africa."

"Moses, Moses not here and now. You may do that somewhere, in another promised land," Afua shouted from the bedroom.

"Amen," uttered Moses, as he slavishly pocketed his prayer book.

Moses clasped Ababi on the shoulders, and said, "My son I'm sorry, some of us are becoming unbelievers."

Moses went to the kitchen, picked up a bottle of beer, and disappeared into the guest room.

There was something strange about Moses. His hair was set and done with some round plastics. Also his face bore strained marks that became intense, whenever he spoke. His neck and shoulders were a resting place for a mass of permed hair. He brushed his fingers through the mass of permed hair and his ears stood like a windmill caught in a gust of wind.

****

Afua changed into an African wear. She walked majestically into the living room.

"Wow, you look gorgeous," Ababi complimented.

"Thank you. Oh it seems we've begun too early. It's only 4:00 PM, but the party starts at 7:00PM."

Ababi grabbed a bunch of newspapers and said, "I guess I wanted to catch the early bird, no, I mean the early worm."

"Don't worry! You will catch many of them. More than you canswallow. But don't vomit in the long run."

"No I won't."

Ababi opened the newspaper and began

to read.

Afua, who was examining some Christmas cards, interrupted him and said, "Won't you wish me a merry Christmas. Anyway I received your card. It's nice of you. It's a marvelous card. Thank you. I will have something special for you after the party. By the way, do you want something to eat while we wait for my other guests to arrive?"

"No, I can't catch worms now. I will wait for other birds to arrive."

Afua got up and pulled the curtains to allow light into the room. As she did so, Ababi noticed scars on Moses' face.

Sensing that something had gone wrong and that Ababi was worried, Afua queried, "Are you okay? Why are you suddenly quiet?"

Ababi shook his head. All the recent memories he had tried to shelve returned. They flooded his mind with debris of incoherence.

Afua was unable to make out what was disturbing him. But she figured it was her skin. Assuredly, but in a confident tone, she stated, "Ababi, get real, these are scars from past bleaching. I told you I don't do it anymore. Or is it the bleaching on Moses' face?"

Ababi declared, "Afua you shouldn't have mentioned his name."

"So what? Is he upset? I don't think so!"

"Oh! Moses. He was a revered Reverend Minister back home in Ghana."

Afua laughed and intoned as if Moses would hear him, and continued, "Rev. Moses joined some American missionaries and their teachings went into his head. The teachings

221

of the church were not based on the Bible, so I hear, but they were based on anideology that blacks were inferior to whites, therefore, should aspire to be whites."

"Now that explains what he said earlier in his prayers for me!"

Afua went into the guest room again, came out and said, "Moses has reached the promised land."

"You mean he is asleep! Wow that's sudden!"

"Let me continue, Rev. Moses came here, and I mean these parts,to achieve the ultimate. But, like me he has had to learn, may benot yet, that we Africans can develop and enjoy our continent to the fullest if we want to. That's if we stop our dependency on these parts."

"Please, Afua, not during this celebration. You don't have to lapse into one of your monologues. Please, no more preaching spiced with apocalyptic visions. Let us celebrate Christmas, a new beginning," Ababi pleaded.

Ababi was always worried about Afua's soul-searching musings that came undisguised and unashamed.

Approaching Afua, Ababi took her hands, and said, "Everythingis okay; everything will be all right," as she broke into sobs, eclipsed by the snoring coming from the guest room.

****

The dissonance of Afua's sobs and Moses' snoring shattered Ababi's peace of mind. His

222

mind roamed in search of all the stories of plentiful, serenity, and joy that one hears in Africa about living in these parts. Yes, ironically, Afua calls it these parts.

****

And Ababi began to go over about the new African dream of travelling to these parts. True, Afua had said that coming to these parts was all about seeking the velvet, the beauty of it, and its magnetic, addictive attractions. Ababi searched for the location of Afua's point of view. But there was none. He felt naive. He would strain himself to learn too. Apparently, there was a price to pay for those who refused to learn. How could people leave their countries, their places of birth, places where they were human beings, and suffer deprivations in alien lands? How could this have happened? The new enslavement, the bondage of the African soul!

****

As Afua's sobbing died down and the snoring from the room gave way to silence, a depressing solitude crept into the apartment.

****

Afua wiped away her tears and intoned, "You know, Moses is snoring like a train that had passed a junction with all its noise to the world. It will return on schedule, another time, because that's its timetable. The snoring follows days of slavery and days when mind, body and soul are turned into machines. Now we're enticed into these parts in many ways."

"Oh! Please, stop sobbing, why this Christmas evening?" "You want to hear that too?"

"Yes, I will be glad to hear from the horse's own mouth."

"Ah, the sobbing comes when it's time to celebrate the comings and goings of the train. Each appearance brings memories wrapped up in tears. It's a way of re-living one's unending miserable journey."

Taking Ababi's hand, Afua asked, "Do you want something more to drink. She started for the kitchen, stopped, and drew other blinds to let in additional light from the balcony.

Moses came out of the guest room and made for the bath room. The lines of stress and anxiety were still on his forehead.

Looking dejected and forlorn, Moses in a yawning tone asked, "Afua, when should we expect the rest of your guests to arrive?"

Afua looked at her wrist watch, laughed aloud, and announced, "They will arrive soon from your promised land, Moses."

Chapter Ten

Afua opened the door and the waves of Christmas air surrounding her guests besieged her room. It was a complete invasion in itself, yet a welcome relief for Ababi!

A man in a three-piece suit, with suffering written all over his face, crested in on the evening Christmas with dizzying enthusiasm. He looked tall. But his height was compromised by the weight of strips of velvets around his neck that were obviously strangling him.

****

Afua had once said that whenever velvet seekers lost their humanity in the hunt for the velvet, immense suffering wrote it on their faces. Although, Ababi did not understand it then, he understood it now. The man's face bore the imprints of that misery.

****

The man began to roam about, going back and forth. He carried himself with an arrogant air of dignity. But there was a twist to his arrogance. Afua, the seer, was very right. She had said that in these parts people masked their sadness with a veneer of happiness.

Craters that inhabited the man's face were carefully filled with face powder. Parts of it had no doubt peeled off. The craters were dotted with pimples, burns, and bristles. His eyes looked like someone who had never slept in his life, or someone who slept but did not close his eyes. The color of his eyes was all the more disturbing; it was amber-like, groping in a pair of holloweye-sockets. His eyeballs appeared to be lurking at the far interior of their sockets like the moon overshadowed by dense clouds.

"I am Professor, that is, Alberts Phillips Williams Musuosons,"the man announced, as he smiled and further explained, "My local Ghanaian name is Kwaku Musuo"

"And, my name is Eh! Ababi," replied Ababi, who didn't know whether to mention his full name as the man had done.

Professor Musuosons's smile cracked the face powder on his hollow cheeks. And he, ritually in a practiced way, touched his face.

****

Ababi began to wonder whether he wanted to remove or affix the face powder.

****

"It will always be like this," Professor Musuosons remarked, as he grimaced and again ritually touched his face.

Professor Musuosons extended his hand to greet Ababi so the latter got up and also extended his hand. Professor Musuosons took Ababi's hand in his wet, frail palm.

"When did you arrive? We've never met

226

before. Have we?""Eh, I arrived exactly four months ago," Ababi replied.

"Call me Prof for short. People here call me that. I don't knowsometimes what they mean by Prof. But it seems to me that they compare my prestigious status in Ghana with the lower one here and laugh at me. Mockery and mockery!"

"Why do you think anyone would want to laugh at you? Youhaven't done anything to deserve that!"

"With sincerity," Prof replied, "I don't know; I have no answers.But I'm certain that I am the object of mockery."

Prof's answer came in gasps. There was pain and suffering, an inner pain and an outer suffering. The gasps came intermittent explosions.

"You see I don't have a teaching job yet," Prof volunteered.

Again, Prof's pain needed no telling. He explained it as if Ababi knew about his perennial quests for teaching positions.

"It's common knowledge that I'm over-qualified for my present job"

"So what type of job are you talking about?"

"I'm a teaching assistant! In fact, the oldest teaching assistant ever! You know, I've thought and wondered about why a distinguished professor like me cannot stay and work at home."

Prof gazed at Ababi, as if he was looking for answers from him,and continued, "It's my personal tragedy, but admittedly it's also that of all Ghanaians and Africans. I pity the taxpayers and the cocoa farmers. It's their collective tragedy too."

****

"Prof, it's your responsibility to bear your tragedy alone," Afua unsympathetically interjected from the other end of the room.

****

Afua thought about how Ko-Ofie was bearing his painful life in these parts alone in a hospital. She had seen him before picking up Ababi and will visit him again the following morning.

****

Prying into Prof's dismal face, Ababi asked, "Prof, where are the rural folks and the cocoa farmers in your story?"

"Oh, the rural folks, they're the cocoa farmers and staple food producers too. You know what cocoa adds to the Ghanaian economy! Yet, the rural folks, the producers, don't have access to hospitals, clinics, bank loans, and may never see cocoa butter and chocolate in their lifetime."

"Well said," Ababi replied.

"We received all the benefits that should have gone to the cocoa-farmers. Why do you think you're here?"

"Please, Prof educate me."

"Well, it's because successive Ghanaian governments exploit cocoa farmers with the backing of governments and institutions of these parts. That's the reason why you're here. It's as simpleas that."

"Prof, I'm afraid I missed your point! What exactly do you mean?"

"I mean that we've got to stay at home and help develop the country so that in the long run, the poor farmers can benefit from us too. The farmers should also get pension and end of service benefits."

****

Afua cleared her throat and said, "It has been six years. I don't think you will get any teaching appointment here. The irony isthat departments interview you for teaching jobs, which you don't get anyway, but continue to contact you and use your ideas."

****

Prof ignored Afua's interjection and said to Ababi, "Anyway, how long did you say you have been here?"

"Four months, I guess," Ababi replied.

"I see, four months, that's why you look very fresh and even raw in a beautiful way."

Ababi laughed uneasily and wondered what was so special about him that made him look fresh and raw. Africans he had met had said that to him many times. But there was some semblance of truth in it. Prof, for example, looked wasted in his own special way. Although, he was plump, his facial stress andstrain told a different story.

****

"Afua, may I have my drink? I mean the special one," Prof called Afua, as he sat limply on the couch.

"Ababi, it's on the kitchen counter. Can you please get it for him," Afua pleaded, and said,

"There is so much to do, but I need to call Ko-Ofie to see how he is doing."

"Yes, you should," Ababi replied, as he got the drink for Prof.

Prof weighed the drink he had received from Ababi and said, "Afua, I think the drink is not enough. I will need another glassful."

"Prof, no problem; Ababi will get it for you."

Quickly, Ababi poured another glassful of drink and gave it to Prof.

Prof gulped down the first glassful of drink and reached for theother one. As he picked up the glassful of drink, his hand shooklike a leaf in a belt of wind.

****

"Afua, can I have another drink, please."

Oh! Prof, your hands are shaking from the abuse of alcohol. I'llgive you another drink, but not right now.

Prof began to sweat profusely.

"No, please, let me have another drink now. I need to calm down my nerves and all the irritating blisters that inhabit my face."

****

Astonished at the blisters on Prof's face, Ababi wondered about why an African of such an academic stature would want to use bleaching creams to get rid of his Africaness.

****

"I used to teach, in fact, lecture at K.N.U.S.T. I studied Philosophy at the University of London, where I obtained my PhD" Prof rolled the last word on his tongue as if he never wanted to part with it, and continued, "I've been here for six years and still looking for a job which suits my qualification. Anyway, I am here alone; my wife and children are at home. It does not matter. Does it? I can go through the suffering alone! It makes it easier."

Prof removed a layer of velvet around his neck and placed it on the arm of the chair. He took one end of the velvet and began to play with it like a child playing with a toy. He examined the velvet clinically, and screamed, "The velvet, velvet, oh, we are the velvet seekers."

****

Afua protested, "Prof, not today! Not at all! This is Christmas! Please, shelve your remorse and pangs of pain, or I'll have to ask you to leave. I can't tolerate it again, not this time around, I am also dealing with pain. You know I have told you Ko-Ofie is sick and hospitalized. Yet, I am not complaining," Afua warned from the bedroom.

****

Torrents of tears besieged Prof's eyes. Using one end of the velvet, he wiped away his tears.

****

Ababi began to understand Afua's longstanding pain, but a professor crying for no apparent reason really shocked him. It was the answer he had been looking for all along. There must be acidic suffering here, indeed, one that kills the soul, but retains the body, what Afua had been saying all along about the livingdead.

****

Summoning courage, Ababi asked, "Prof, what're you doing to yourself?"

"Oh, you've been here for only few months and yet you have the courage to ask me this type of question? What are you here for?"

"I'm a student". "What do you study?" "History."

"European? Western history?"

"African."

"I see, you are here on scholarship."

"Yes, Ghanaian government scholarship."

****

Afua intervened and said "Ababi, please give me a hand in the kitchen."

Ababi, in turn said, "Prof excuse me for a second."

As soon as Ababi got to the kitchen, Afua whispered, "Prof gets inflamed with such issues so don't have any discussions with him."

"Is he the only one? Don't you all?"

"Well, say what you wish to say. The fact is, like many of us, he is totally disappointed in these parts. But, unlike many of us, Prof always wants an audience that will pity him. If you want to enjoy your Christmas, just avoid him."

****

Prof took a glance at Ababi and asked, "Is there something more to drink; I mean something special to drink?"

****

"Come to the kitchen and serve yourself. You've no servants here," Afua shouted.

Prof went to the kitchen, opened the deep-freezer, and remarked, "Afua, you've only beer!"

Prof took a bottle of beer and squeezed its lid open.

"Oh, I cut myself," Prof revealed, as he rushed to the living room to take his velvet. Placing the velvet on the bruised finger, Prof began to smile as if nothing had happened.

****

"Prof go to the bathroom and wash away the blood," Afua ordered.

"I think the velvet will do. Blood is very important and must not be washed away, especially in strange lands."

Afua looked on unamused. She knew that if she persisted, Prof would give a whole lecture on the purity of African blood in these parts.

Leaving the kitchen, Ababi went to see what Prof was describing as a ritual. To his surprise, it was one of Prof's bloated blisters from bleaching, that had given off its contents, but not that the lid had cut into his skin.

Ababi looked down and shuffled his feet on the floor, as Prof smiled wryly at him. In spite of his disapproval of Prof's behavior, Ababi had some respect for him because professors are a repository of knowledge and academic power.

Prof gulped down the beer at a go, but could not swallow all. The cascade of beer drained the corners of his mouth.

Ababi whose eyes were following the beer streaming down Prof's cheeks, was suddenly startled by a disturbing knock on the door.

****

As Ababi opened the door, Afua shouted, "Hi, Tokey, you came at last."

"Hey, Prof yar ready here?"

"Yes, Tokey, I've been here since noon."

"Why don ya respect the velvet? Why ya soaking im with bload?"

234

"Oh for God's sake what do you know about blood," Prof. exclaimed.

"Ain't here to talk aba bload, or discuss what I know aba bload, okay. Am `here to celebate ma own Xmas. Yeah men, special abruord Xmas, not ya Ghana type. So ya better shat up with yaprofessorsims."

****

"Hey Afua, melly Xmas, ya place is net as decolated like ma place. Where is ma good fiend Dr. Ko-Ofie? Ya come to my decolated place. Ya better come and see it for ya self. What abatthirty oneth December? Yeah free invitation, take it, it's free from me," Tokey declared as he embraced Afua.

"No, Tokey, I've no intention of visiting your palatial place. Anyway Ko-Ofie is on admission at a hospital. And can't you speak Twi? Your English makes mockery of all that is nice in languages," Afua replied as she gently pushed away Tokey.

Turning to Ababi, Afua began to laugh derisively.

Ababi put his middle finger on his lips, indicating that Afua should stop laughing, and said, "I think I'm lost in this cold world where people come to acquire civilization!"

Tokey walked towards Ababi, but for some reason, paused to give him a clinical look.

Realizing the strange look in Tokey's eyes, Ababi extended his hand and said, "I'm Ababi, nice to meet you."

"Erm, I'm Tokey for short, well tha's what

ya Africans call me, but the white folks call me Allight Hope Tokey, I'm pleased to meet ya in camera."

Tokey paused for effect and declared, "Blother men, ya're not lost at all. Time tells everything. Just ya forgot what's done to us here and be some happy person. Tha's wha life is all aboaut."

Controlling her laughter, Afua replied, "You know, my husband, Ko-Ofie, made a good point, when he said that the more illiterate one was, the more one imitated whites."

Ignoring Afua's statement, Tokey intoned, "Prof Melly Xmas. Well, Prof and Afua, and ya new guy," as he pointed to Ababi, "This is ma girlie, I mean girlflend. She is white."

Afua laughed, but stopped, and in a mocking tone asserted, "Oh Tokey, stop it. All of us have eyes, and even if we don't, we can smell one when we see one. What have you learnt from her? Is it how not to speak good English?"

****

In the midst of these exchanges Prof sat down and began to clean his face with the velvet. As he cleaned his forehead with a tissue paper, pain and anguish gripped the very contours of his face.

"Ah, Afua, I'm suffering," Prof. lamented, as he looked briefly at the velvet around his neck.

"Oh! Prof, will you please keep quiet with your self-inflicted pain? All of you make me

236

sick, do you hear me."

****

Ababi looked at Afua and courteously asked, "Prof, what pain?"Prof pointed at his face, and explained, "These are no pimples! They are sores of my own making."

Afua intervened and calmly, but with authority stated, "Prof, please, those are not sores. It's your new identity. It's an attemptto trade your African identity for a white one."

Eyeing Ababi, Afua carefully chose and stressed her words, stating that, "You are a historian. You know about the slave trade! I guess this time around they restrain us, but we come willingly. And it is still pain and suffering. These things we do to ourselves!"

****

Tokey, who was listening, chimed in and said, "Oh! Afua, no more talk talk about slave trade, ya hear me. My white girl don't like that."

Pointing to the beer in the grip of Tokey's girlfriend, Afua explained calmly, "You see this beer, it dulls the mind like enslavement. Your mind is dull Tokey. I'm talking about the modern slave trade that brings us here in new slave ships. Yousee, we are the living dead. We are the walking dead. We die here long before we go home. We take the ghosts of these parts to our respective homes in Africa. And our apparitions are shadowing the continent along pathways of doom."

Tokey looked on gloomily and managed to ask, "Afua, what do ya mean? What's happened to ya? Ya going crazy too like Prof, Dr. Ko-Ofie, and them all?"

****

Prof yawned, left the living room, and disappeared into the vicinity of the bedrooms.

As all eyes followed Prof, Tokey moved closer to his girlfriend and said, "Afua, this is no place to disglace us. We all know why we ya here. No slave trade ploblems! So if ya've any sickness ploblems, save it until ya've a healer."

Afua replied, "Oh! So now you know about healing? Eh! I thought you lost it long ago. And that you can't even think. It's good to know that Christmas in these parts brings new ideas."

Satisfied that his explanation had been accepted by Afua, Tokey continued with the introduction of his girlfriend, "All of ya hear meet Annatoto," he said.

"Anna who?" asked Afua with a smile.

"The name is Annatoto, but she's called Anna for short."

****

Prof made his way back to the living room and leaned against the wall, as tears welled in his tired eyes.

Afua pitied Prof for all his pain and suffering. She bent down her head and wiped away her own tears before they dropped.

****

As quietly as he had come in, Prof disappeared into the guest bedroom.

****

Ababi followed the movement of Prof with his eyes, and asked, "Is this how you celebrate Christmas here?" Ababi was surprised at the way his first Christmas was turning out to be both on the way to and in Afua's home. Unbelievably, it was turning into a sorrowful event, instead of a celebration of the birth of Christ. And instead of happiness, everyone was on thewings of sadness!

****

Then, Ababi asked, "What's happening here?"

"You can never understand. You have to wait a little while," Afua replied, as she focused on Annatoto.

****

Ababi was not sure. He couldn't help it. Time and again, he had asked himself why Prof and all others were in these parts ifthey really knew what was happening to them! Could it be thatthey were clamoring for any crumb they can find in these parts?Sane men and women removed from their happy homes and forced into the throes of pain and humiliation.

****

Annatoto felt very uncomfortable from the way Afua was gazing at her.

Afua had no intention of hiding her piercing and accusing eyes. Annatoto was very big, yet carried herself well. The bursting seams of the huge and frocky African dress, that harbored her, looked grotesquely beautiful. Her blonde hair cascaded down her bulging shoulders. Perching on her wide forehead was a big, bedecking pair of dark glasses.

Afua maintained her keen look at Annatoto, as she headed for the kitchen, and called out, "Ababi, come in here."

"Okay!"

"Please serve Tokey and his girl for me," Afua pleaded, as she removed plates from the kitchen shelve.

Before Ababi could ask them, Tokey answered, "Oh, I'll have anytin, bat, Anna likes her special drink called the Caribbean. Afua ya knaw wat I mean."

Walking briskly from the kitchen, Afua countered, "What do you mean. Do you think this is one of those pick-up bars? I don't have any Jamaican or Bermuda drinks. You Ghanaian men do anything for these Annatoto women, but when it comes to us you don't give a shit!"

"Ya it is becurse, you don't knaw haw to

laave, see," as he pointed to Annatoto, "These are vely gad laavers. Can't ya see her hair, long flawing hair? See her lips, see her color, and see her talk. No, and I won't stand here quietly as you insult me and ma girlie sensibles, you hear me. You can do tha with ya hoseband Ko-Ofie."

Tokey, pausing for effect, looked at Annatoto and concluded, "Afua for ya informations, I braught my own Caribben dlink."

"Oh! Then you better go and bring it. You can bring the whole Caribbean here," Afua laughed, as she walked back to the kitchen.

"Hi!"

Afua overheard Annatoto's deep, indoor voice and turned around to face her.

"Hi, what can I do for you?"

"You can't do anything for me and you've nothing to offer me. I just wanna tell you to be polite and to show that your stay here has improved your civility and manners. That's if you ever had done before coming here!"

Surprised at Annatoto's statements, Ababi cut in and pleaded, "Err, please, this is Christmas; there is no need for us to quarrel. Let us all enjoy ourselves in peace."

Afua pushed Ababi aside as gently as she could, and stated, "We are not fighting here, not at all. If I want to fight, I would not fight this white woman. Yes, I'm aware that the fatty ones tend to be more intolerant than the slim ones in the midst of African men when African women are present,"

Annatoto surveyed Afua, cleared her throat, and said, "You these people from that shithole called Africa! You think I'm a bigot? No! That's not the issue. The issue is that those of you who can't tolerate our superiority are the ones that suffer here. Look at Tokey, yes, look at Allbright Hope. He is a happy person, I mean a happy black man who doesn't worry about my superiority and white supremacy?"

Afua returned Annatoto's gaze and asked, "Did you say we are from a shithole and that Tokey is happy? Leave out Tokey. Why is it that fat white women like you rejected by your civilized society because they think that you are too huge and even ugly always cash in on marginalized African men? This is where Tokey comes in, right?" It is you who come from a gilded shithole you call civilization.

Annatoto responded, "I may be fat, but the fact remains that I'm blonde, and above all I'm white and superior." "Please stop or else I may have to leave," Ababi warned.

Looking straight at Ababi, then focusing on Annatoto, Afua replied, "Who cares, you may leave if you want to. I won't stop you. Not at all! I am sick and tired of people like you who keep running away from those who seek to marginalize and demonize us."

Suddenly, Tokey appeared with the special Caribbean drink for Annatoto.

Seeing the Caribbean drink, Annatoto refocused on Afua, and explained, "I like this drink. It always reminds me of my vacation in Trinidad. May be when I visit another backwater, and it may be Jamaica, Bermuda, Barbados, St Kitts, or any of our vacation colonies, you can make me another

Caribbean drink?"

Tokey cut in and said, "Oh, for sure, I'll always make one for ya. It's good tha ya guys go those places. In fact, it's a plocess of civilizetion for them, and I don knaw why ya guys don come to Africa backwaters. We also have rivers at the back and the sea in the front."

Ababi, who was going to the kitchen to bring a drinking glass for Annatoto, stopped short and said, "Oh, please don't say that. That is not true. Civilization is relative and no one cultureis better than the other. And you should know that people are the products of their environments."

"Don't waste your breath on Tokey," Afua interjected sharply, as she headed for the bedroom.

Ignoring Afua's comments, Tokey asked, "When are ya other black Africans coming?"

Holding onto the frames of the bedroom door, Afua replied caustically, Allbright Hope Tokey, don't worry, the second coming of the black Africans to labor in these parts is already happening."

****

In the bedroom, Afua thought about the Caribbean drink, the vacation in the Caribbean backwaters, what Tokey had called civilization, and tears welled up in her eyes.

****

A knock at the bedroom door derailed Afua's suffusing thoughts, as she uttered, "Please come in. Is that you, Ababi?"

Ababi walked in without answering to his name.

"Why are you crying? Do you miss your husband, Ko-Ofie?" Ababi asked tenderly.

"Oh, my God! I do. I will visit him tomorrow morning. Will youdo me a favor by accompanying me? You see none of my guests really cares about Ko-Ofie's illness," Afua intoned sadly.

"May be it's because of the greetings, welcomes and the arguments. Don't you think so," Ababi asked unconvincingly, but in a soothing tone.

"No, I don't think so. I think the inhumanity, the individualism,and alienation here, have affected all of us," Afua paused to wipe away tears welling up in her eyes.

"So why are you crying?"

"Oh, it was because of what Annatoto said about vacations and all that civilization stuff."

"Wow! You are becoming one of the most passionate Africanist.

You cry over that! I can't believe it!"

"I may not be an Africanist, but I love my Africa. I don't even know why I am orbiting these parts."

"Oh! Don't say that Afua."

Afua, ignored Ababi and emphasized, "Yes I miss my Africa. I love my African. And no"

"I think you're and a very good Africanist."

****

Tokey knocked on Afua's bedroom door.

Ababi opened the door and seeing that it was Tokey amusingly asked, "Oh! Tokey! Why? Have you finished your Caribbean drink?"

"Tokey grinning replied, "No Ababi, ma girlie's drinking it. More visitors have alived, about six people."

Afua laughed and said, "Oh! Tokey, why can't you speak a Ghanaian language with us? Visitors are obviously people. Please, Ababi get them something to drink, while I dress up."

As Ababi approached the living room, he was dazzled by the velvety-dressed guests. They wore various kinds of ornaments, especially necklaces that looked as big as dog chains. In fact, they were resplendently dressed, more than Prof, but similar to that of Tokey. They shared one thing in common: bleached complexions and weird wigs. Their manners of speech shocked Ababi as the conversations among them revealed their affected Western accents. It was a strange ABC accent transposed onto an odd BBC one. Above all, they had pieces of velvets of various colors, bedecking and weighing down their necks.

Ababi had wanted to ask them about what they would drink, but changed his mind and said to them, "Please feel free, drinks are in the fridge. Afua will be with you in a moment."

One of the newly-arrived guests asked, "Oh, do you have German wine?"

245

Ababi politely told the man, "I'm also a guest," but mockingly added, "How about some Ghanaian wine?"

"No, I am asking for German wine. You mean you want meto drink Ghanaian wine here. Who cares to drink that? I'msure you are new here. I was in Germany before coming here. It's the best wine in the world, but now my white girlfriend is introducing me to French wine."

"I'm sorry, I don't know the difference between French and German wine, even if I did, I would all the same give you Ghanaian wine. This is because I've not been Germanized nor Frenchized yet," Ababi replied sarcastically.

The man retorted, "Well, some of us are," as he walked to the kitchen to look for something to drink.

****

Ababi returned to the bedroom and quipped, "Afua, you musthave selected your guests from the outer frontiers of knowledge. And indeed, they are here for their second coming."

"Why, Ababi?"

"Well, Afua, please come and listen to your guests' wishes and needs. I'm going out there to be with them."

Ababi waved at Afua, and stepped into the living room. He surveyed the guests and politely said, "Please Afua has food and drinks in the kitchen."

246

****

As Ababi walked towards the kitchen, one of the newly arrived guests introduced himself, "My name is Liverpool.""Oh, eh, is that so? My name is Ababi."

"So, what do you do here?"

"I'm a student."

"Don't you have a Christian name? What do you study?"

Surprised, Ababi shot back, "You mean a Christian name like Liverpool?"

"Oh! Exactly! Exactly! And what do you study?"

"Well, I tell stories; in fact, I'm a historian, or hope to be one." "You mean you traveled all the way here to study story-telling!""I think so," replied Ababi who was growing impatient.

Liverpool laughed aloud, composed himself, and said, "My friend, find some work to do. The fact is that all of us come here to work. Not to mention that some of us are selling our bodies, and oh, some sell drugs, and also dupe insurance companies. You know they exploited Africa so now is the time to exploit them too. But the basic fact is that we survive all the same."

"May I know the type of work you do in these parts?"

"I work at a fast food joint as dishwasher."

"Well, good for you; I don't blame you. I will rather tell my stories as they are, and though I may sound rude, I think you need washing too," Ababi countered.

****

Suddenly, Afua, ended the looming uneasiness, as she hilariously shouted, "Hello everybody, let the Christmas party begin now."

Afua held one end of her velvet, while the other end swept the floor.

"Hey, play some music. No Ghanaian hi life, but Amelican pop songs," Tokey requested enthusiastically.

When Afua reached where Prof was standing, she let go the velvet and extended her hands to Prof.

As Prof got up to dance, Afua said, "Many of my guests have not arrived yet. As the years go by so do my guests come in late, as if they have lost interest in my annual Christmas get together!"

Strutting like an underfed pig, Prof raised his hands and began to circle around Afua who was dancing with abandonment.

Afua looked at Prof and said, "So many things have happened. It's not easy for us to hear Christmas bells ringing anymore. We are immune to everything around us. We suffer inner pain, anguish and tribulations."

****

Afua left Prof on the dancing floor, touched Ababi's neck, and smiled and said, "Only the new, the young, and the raw like you see things differently. And it's our fault."

"Oh, don't say that."

Again poking Ababi's ribs, Afua

continued, "Soon, you will come to learn that even Christmas like so many things, for us, has got its wretched side in these parts."

****

Afua's words were cut short by the piercing ringing noise of her cellphone. She stopped dancing and picked up it.

Across the other half of the living room, Liverpool and Tokey were humming an improvised dirge after a Christmas song.

Afua cleared her throat, asked Ababi to turn down the volume of the music, and added, "Liverpool and Tokey please keep quiet while I take the phone call?"

But Tokey only stopped for a moment and headed for the kitchen and began to sing the dirge again. Leaning on the kitchen door, he abandoned the improvised dirge and began to sing a well- known dirge in Twi, his Ghanaian language.

Afua looked at Tokey pensively, but realized nothing could stop him.

"Hello, what err," then Afua clung onto the cellphone, and appeared momentarily frozen.

Suddenly, the cellphone fell from her hands. For some seconds, she flung her hands like someone trapped in a quicksand and in search of immediate rescue.

Afua appeared lost. The noise and organized chaos around her no longer mattered. She sat unconcernedly on the floor, entombed by gilded velvets of different kinds and colors.

In an act of defiant desperation, Afua threw down her velvet. She looked at it for a long time, turned to face her guests, and whispered, "Ah! Ko-Ofie, has gone into a coma!"

Ababi hurried to her side and said, "He will be ok. Don't worry, he will be ok."

"Yes, he is orbiting these parts."